the
gravedigger's
story

Ged Simmons

First published in 2004 by I.M.P. FICTION
I.M.P. Fiction is an imprint of I.M.P. Publishing Ltd.

ISBN 0-9533275-8-2

Printed and bound in Great Britain.

Edited by Kaye Roach

I.M.P. Fiction Ltd
P. O. Box 14691, London, SE1 2ZA
Fax: 01440 788 562   E-mail: info@impbooks.com

Visit I.M.P. FICTION at: www.impbooks.com

The Gravedigger's Story

by

Ged Simmons

I.M.P. FICTION
London

Author's Acknowledgements

Thanks to Ben Livingstone for years of feedback and encouragement; to Sophie Hicks for believing in Mason; and to Kaye and Martin Roach for running with him.

For Dad, Mom, Pete, Keir, Jenny and Mark.

PART ONE

1

After I kill my Dadda, I'm going to kill myself.

He isn't my real father and until very recently I hadn't seen him for more than thirty years.

I hope you will understand my reasons.

2

Like most young women my mother discovered sex in her early teens. Unlike most teenagers at the latter end of the nineteen fifties she also engaged in sexual activity, prolifically and indiscriminately. I've no doubt she derived physical pleasure from the act but what she enjoyed even more was the power her sexuality gave her over men. And she used this power, teasing and tantalising, to get whatever it was a teenage girl found desirable back then. If she'd had more imagination or experience she might have done better out of the situation.

The other reason she delighted in her promiscuity was because it was in direct contradiction to her strict Catholic upbringing. If my grandparents had known what she was up to they would have crucified her. As it was they didn't find out until it was too late to avoid the catastrophe of my conception.

.....

Being a pregnant seventeen-year-old was much more difficult then than it is now. There were few, if any organisations offering confidential help, advice or, more to the point, safe methods of dealing with the predicament. My mother had heard about the various unsavoury backstreet methods of getting rid of an unwanted foetus - bottles of gin, hot baths, wire coat-hangers - but she didn't have the stomach for any of these. Fortunately, for both of us, she understood the risks and dangers. However, she also knew that once she told her parents, abortion would not be an option. She put it off for months, understandably worried about revealing her terrible secret, but there came a point when she had no choice; she was living at home, earning a pittance working in a shop and it was soon going to be impossible to disguise the obvious. She could, of course, have eloped with my father – my genetic father – or married him. The only problem with that was that she didn't know who he was. And the field of possibilities wasn't narrow. (When I was growing up she used to look for similarities between me and some of her former lovers but she never spotted anything conclusive. The owner of the loins from which I sprang remains as much a mystery to her as it does to me.)

·····

My grandparents' immediate reaction was shock, followed by fury, followed by demands to know who was responsible. When my mother told them she didn't know, and why she didn't know they were astounded. Horrified. They couldn't believe she had been so prolific in her sexual activities that she honestly had no idea. This was their daughter! A good Catholic girl who went to mass every Sunday and confession every fortnight! The whole idea was beyond them; in keeping with their beliefs they had both retained their virginity until they were married.

My grandfather was all for going out and dragging in each and every candidate and 'beating the shite out of them' until one of them admitted responsibility. This was until someone pointed out to him that the young men in question wouldn't know either.

The initial shock was followed by the realisation of the scandal they would face. A pregnant unmarried daughter. That would soon set the tongues to wagging. There was talk of sending my mother to stay with relatives in Ireland for the duration of her confinement; however, it was decided that the shame of the family back home knowing was even worse than the local community finding out.

What could they do?

My grandfather asked if there wasn't a steady boyfriend who might be up for marrying her anyway? Or someone they could con into believing he was the father? My mother told him there wasn't. Unfortunately her reputation was well established and, much as I'm sure she had many admirers, I doubt any of them would have been stupid enough to accept responsibility for the conception of her unborn child, or the responsibilities of providing for it once it was born.

By the fifth month of the pregnancy they still hadn't worked out what to do. I wasn't showing too noticeably at that stage but it was only a matter of time before people cottoned on. Then, one drunken night, in a moment of uncharacteristic openness, my grandfather poured out his heart to a neighbour over a late night drink. It was a problem he didn't know how to deal with. What they needed was either, God forbid, for my mother to lose the child or else to find someone to marry her.

The neighbour was a man of forty-two whose wife had died in childbirth fifteen years earlier. The baby, a girl who would have been named Laura after her mother, died at the same time. Their deaths nearly destroyed him; it was a blow from which he had never fully recovered and as a consequence of which he had never re-married. He was a quiet kindly man who was known in the area for his generosity and willingness to help others. His name was, and is, Stephen Preskett. He is my Dadda.

.....

When Dadda offered to marry my mother I'm sure he had no unwholesome thoughts about how wonderful it would be to marry an attractive younger woman. And she was attractive. I imagine his only consideration was that Grandpa was a friend with a problem and by marrying his daughter he could help solve that problem.

My grandparents discussed it over the next few days. The only real sticking point was that not only was Dadda not Catholic, even worse he was a confirmed atheist. However, on the plus side, he was a known quantity, he lived a few doors away, he was a well-respected member of the community, he had a trade which gave him a steady income and, most importantly, he declared he had no sexual interest in my mother. When they had to sell the idea to her this was a significant factor.

At first she laughed; the idea was ridiculous. Then, when she realised her parents were deadly serious, she threw tantrums, crying and screaming. But, in the end, she agreed. Despite her rebellious nature she was only too aware of the stigma of being an unmarried mother and she didn't want to be lumbered with that. She agreed to marry Dadda and live in his house with the proviso that if she lost the child she would move immediately back to Grandma and Grandpa's.

.....

My mother hoped she'd lose the child. She cursed the day I was born. She didn't want to be a parent and she didn't want to be married to Dadda. And to all intents and purposes, for the first seven years of my life, she got her way.

.....

In the last ten years I have had only one real friend. His name's Tom and he never knew his natural father either. His real dad fell from a roof when Tom was ten months old, landing head first on a metal grate, cracking his skull and squishing his brains like meat through a mincer. Tom's mother re-married a few years later and had three more children, so Tom has a half-brother and two half-sisters. His mother and stepfather treated them all with equal love and affection and, until his mother died, Tom visited them most weekends.

3

Dadda was a carpenter, a man with a true appreciation of nature. He took satisfaction from his daily labours - making doors, windows, frames and so on - but he got his pleasure in discovering the essence of a raw chunk of wood. He would spend hours running his hands over a twisted lump of root or branch, feeling the grain, the knots, the texture of the bark, allowing the wood to speak to him. Then he employed his skills with the lathe or a stout, sharp knife to shape it into something beautiful. That was his real joy.

One of the most enduring images I have of Dadda is of him sitting on his shed step in the warmth of a summer's day, whittling wood and smoking his pipe as he listened to my childish chatter. Only stopping to answer my questions. He always answered my questions.

Some of the things he made were functional – such as fruit bowls or a set of salad servers – but mostly they were ornamental; things of beauty in themselves. There was a dog's head – a spaniel I think. A tiny oak tree, solid and lovely to hold; I remember thinking it was like a hard, smooth cauliflower. An intricate copy of an old man's hand; not modelled on his own hands, which were big and fleshy, toughened by work. The hand he carved was much smaller and frailer. There were birds and wild animals but my favourite piece was a fabulous magical castle – with turrets and conical towers and an arched gateway – which rose up from a rocky knoll. Dadda made it for me and I still have it.

4

Between Rufus Road and Astor Road the houses of Manning Road stand in one long, unbroken terrace. Dadda's house, number 163, was next to one of the covered entries that give access to the back gardens. Five doors down – towards Astor Road – was my grandparents' house, which was also next to an entry.

At the time I lived there the houses were all pretty much identical: front room, living room and kitchen downstairs; two bedrooms and a bathroom upstairs.

.....

My mother slept in the front bedroom that I shared with her for the first few months of my life. She wasn't keen on breast-feeding but both Grandma and the midwife were insistent on it; however, as soon as I started taking a bottle I was moved into the back bedroom with Dadda, who took all responsibility for me during the night.

Before he married my mother he used to sleep in the front bedroom but he swapped on her insistence; she didn't want the back bedroom, through which you had to go to get to the bathroom, because she didn't want him "traipsing through, disturbing me if he wanted a pee in the middle of the night".

.....

The kitchen door opened onto the yard from which there were three steps up to a small paved area and the lawn. Dadda's shed stood at the top of the lawn, which was flanked by carefully tended flowerbeds. It was a pretty garden where I loved to spend time; jumping up and down the steps, playing on the lawn, exploring among the shrubbery, talking idly to Dadda if he was outside or hanging around the shed doorway if he was working inside.

The only time I remember my mother going into the garden was on the rare occasion that she grudgingly hung out the washing; although she later claimed to have spent time sunbathing at the bottom of the yard, "hidden from nosey neighbours".

.....

I'm not sure what my first memory is. Tom claimed he could remember lying in his cot, looking up at a mobile of brightly coloured boats and reckoned he was two years old at the time. I wonder if that's a real memory or something he's been told by his mum. I find it hard to believe that someone can remember that far back. My early memories are all mixed up. Most are just vague impressions: the excitement generated by the arrival of our first television in the corner of the living room; being in church, transfixed by the colours of the stained-glass window illuminated by the morning sun; a white and black boxer dog jumping up playfully and knocking me over. I don't know exactly when these things happened and I can't remember any more specific details about them.

In what I believe to be my earliest memory I know I was able to talk quite well and I'm fairly sure it happened before I started school, so I imagine I must have been about four.

It was a summer's day. Dadda was in the shed sharpening some of his tools and I was in a little world of my own, playing make-believe games on the lawn and in the flowerbeds. As I was crawling around under one of the bushes I found a dead butterfly. (Is it just me or are there less butterflies around these days? I hardly ever see any now but there always seemed to be butterflies in Dadda's garden in the summer.) It was perfectly intact and for a long time I sat on the edge of the grass inspecting it, admiring the markings on its wings and marvelling at the fragility of it. Eventually Dadda popped his head around the shed door.

"What have you got there?" he asked.

I showed him and he told me it was a Red Admiral. I must have taken this on board because, to this day, the Red Admiral is the only butterfly I can identify. However, at the time, I was more concerned with metaphysical matters.

.....

I don't know when I was first taken to mass; sometime when I was an infant, I suppose. Grandma was keen that my indoctrination into the Catholic faith should start early. And this wasn't restricted to church on Sundays; she took every opportunity to teach me 'the word', telling me bible stories, teaching me the Ten Commandments and explaining the Holy Trinity and the concepts of heaven, hell and purgatory.

.....

"Will it go to heaven?" I asked Dadda.

"No."

"Why not?"

"Because there is no heaven."

I thought about this for a moment.

"Where will it go then?"

"It won't go anywhere, unless the wind blows it away."

He must have sensed my alarm and added:

"There's nothing to be afraid of, son. Everything dies. That's just part of nature."

"Where will I go when I die?" I asked him.

"That'll be up to you. You can either be buried in a grave or burned in a special place called a crematorium."

"Will it hurt if they burn me?"

"No. You won't know anything about it. You'll be dead."

"I don't think I'd like to be burned."

"That's all right, you don't have to be. You can choose what you want when you grow up."

I sat in silence for a while, contemplating the butterfly and thinking about what Dadda had said. He never tried to shelter me from the truth. He'd told me about death, burial and cremation in a gentle matter-of-fact way, but I was having trouble reconciling this with what I'd been told by my grandmother.

"Grandma says if we're good we go to heaven after we die."

"I don't think there is a heaven, son. Your Grandma believes there is. When you're old enough you can decide for yourself what you believe. Just remember this: all living things die. People. Butterflies. Everything. We're all part of nature, Mason, and I think that's where we go when we die: back to nature. Not to a lovely place called Heaven or a terrible place called Hell. I think the church tells people that to scare them into behaving in a certain way. But I think you have to behave in the way that you think is good and right."

He smiled at me, took his pipe from his pocket, lit it and puffed clouds of richly aromatic smoke while we sat quietly, letting things sink in.

.....

Despite his own lack of faith Dadda never questioned the fact that I was brought up Catholic and he never tried to undermine it. He wouldn't dismiss out of hand other people's beliefs or theories; he just made me aware that there were alternatives and told me I should investigate all the possibilities. The only thing was, when he explained anything he did so with such patience and clarity and quiet assurance that it always sounded right.

.....

"What shall we do with it?" I asked, cupping the butterfly in my hands.

"Well, we could leave it to see if the wind blows it away. Or, if you want, we could bury it. Or burn it."

"What will happen if we bury it?"

"It'll rot away slowly," he told me.

"Is that what happens to people?"

"If they're buried, yes. Or the worms eat them."

"Worms?!"

"It's all right. The people can't feel it; they're dead."

"Will you be buried, Dadda?"

"Well, I like worms because they're good for my garden but, no, I think I'd like to be cremated."

I thought about this before declaring:

"I don't like either."

"That's all right, you've got plenty of time to think about it."

I considered the delicate, brightly coloured Red Admiral resting on the palm of my hand.

"I don't want to burn it, Dadda. Can we bury it?" I asked.

"Of course we can."

We chose a place in one of the flowerbeds, near to the shed and I dug a little hole with a trowel while Dadda emptied the matches from his box of Swan Vestas. He placed the butterfly carefully in the matchbox, put it into the hole and I covered it with soil.

I had dug my first grave and that, I believe, is my first memory.

5

These days I am a creature of habit. My daily routine rarely changes: I wake every morning between 6.30 and 6.45; I put the kettle on;

15

wash; dress; make a pot of tea; eat a breakfast of cereal, a boiled egg and two pieces of toast; make my sandwiches (usually two ham and mustard and two cheese and pickle, or sometimes I have tinned fish); I wash my dishes; pack my shoulder bag; collect any rubbish in a plastic carrier bag; put on my coat; get my spade from beside the door; and leave around 7.30am. I walk the three miles to work, travelling the length of Manning Road on the way, passing the house that I used to live in with Dadda and I arrive at St. Angela's just after 8.10am. I usually make a brew on the little camping stove in my shed and I'm at work before 8.30am. On my way home I pick up eight cans of lager which I drink after I've cleared up the dinner things. Sometimes I have a glass or two of whisky as well. I spend my evenings reading, listening to music or watching a film on television. I only ever watch films. (I never buy newspapers or magazines so I tear the TV guide out of the free paper that's pushed through the door every week.) If I can't sleep, as is often the case, I go for a walk.

About once a fortnight I go to the library to take out, renew or return books. I read almost anything fictional. Some of it's rubbish but in the main it's fairly literary. I have read quite a few 'classics'; not that I've enjoyed or understood them all. I have no interest in current affairs, history, other people's lives, politics or any other type of non-fiction. I never buy books; they'd only clutter up my room. The only books I do possess are a well-thumbed dictionary and a book about photography, which is the only thing I own that was given to me by my mother. I keep it because it is about one of the few hobbies I ever had. I also have several photograph albums.

On Saturday nights I go to The Grouse And Gun pub where I sit next to the fireplace and read. During the winter months there's usually a real log fire burning. I used to meet Tom in The Grouse And Gun when we were still friends.

On Sundays - my one day off a week - I do my washing, by hand, in the bathroom that I share with two other people. That's my only regular weekly chore as I shop and keep my room tidy on a day-to-day basis.

The room itself is on the first floor of a three-storey building that has been converted into bedsits. I have a sink which doubles as a urinal late at night; I scour it with bleach to make sure it doesn't smell. There is a bed, a plywood wardrobe, a rickety chest of drawers, a hard-backed chair and a dining table that the television set sits on. The magnolia-painted walls are bare of decoration but I've put up some shelves to hold my cassettes, my radio/cassette player, my two books, my photograph albums and my carvings. These include several pieces I've carved myself and two that were made by Dadda: the magic castle and one other piece.

There is a communal kitchen in the building but I prefer to cook in my room, using an old electric Baby Belling cooker with two rings and an oven/grill. I'm someone who eats to live, not the other way around, so I'm quite happy with simple, stodgy food. If I fancy something a bit more exotic I can always get a take-away, but that's rare.

Considering the house was converted with cheap materials I hear relatively little noise from the other tenants. I'm probably lucky in that my room is bounded on three sides by the original brick walls. Many of the other interior walls in the house are made of plasterboard.

My window overlooks a school on the other side of the street. Not that I ever see the children as I'm gone before they arrive and they're gone by the time I get home. I have few happy memories of school.

6

While we lived with Dadda I had several pets – hamsters, mice and a guinea pig – all of which eventually joined the butterfly somewhere in the flowerbeds, along with a variety of birds and insects I found in the garden. It became something of an obsession. I must have buried quite a few animals before I ever saw the gravedigger, which might explain my fascination with him and why, unlike the other kids on our street, I wasn't afraid of him.

I would have liked a dog but my mother wouldn't have one in the house and, after we left Dadda, there were no pets of any description. She said keeping animals cooped up was cruel which, I suppose, was a fairly enlightened point of view; not that

I understood it at the time. If I persisted with my pleading she would say there was enough mess and bother already without having to clean up after an animal as well. I suspect the real reason was that she didn't want the responsibility of looking after it. It was bad enough having to look after me; not that she approached the task with any enthusiasm or care. Once we'd left Dadda I quickly developed a degree of independence – encouraged by my mother - that was well in advance of my age.

I'm not allowed to keep pets in the room I'm living in now. I could probably get away with something small and easily maintained, like a fish or a budgie, but I have no interest any more. The cemetery is bordered on one side by open fields and there are lots of trees around the place so I see plenty of birds, squirrels, rabbits and other wildlife. Thanks to Tom I'm able to identify most of the birds. Although I'm not as interested in them as he is I used to enjoy telling him what species I'd seen recently, or describing ones I didn't recognise so he could name them for me. For him it's a real passion.

7

As a small child I had no idea that our home life was any different to other families'. That my mother and Dadda slept in separate rooms; that I shared Dadda's room; that my mother hardly seemed to be at home; that Grandma did a lot of our housekeeping and looked after me; these things didn't seem unusual. Why should they? I had no reason to expect otherwise.

I never saw my mother argue with Dadda - not even a mild disagreement - but I imagine that was all thanks to him. After she took me away from him I saw her have many screaming rows and fights with subsequent partners, which was a more genuine reflection of her real nature.

I don't remember Dadda ever losing his temper. I saw him hurt himself, accidentally, on a couple of occasions but he bore the pain with quiet fortitude. That was his nature.

I suppose he was quite a melancholic man but there was always an air of good humour about him and he liked to laugh. I have often wondered what he must have been like before the Lauras died.

Physically he was bigger than average, without being enormous. He had a lived-in, pleasant face; thin, light-brown hair; a slightly flattened nose; full lips; and clear, pale green eyes. When he laughed his eyes shimmered like the surface of a pool that has been disturbed by a soft breeze. But my favourite thing about him were his hands; strong and gnarled - like some of the lumps of wood he brought home - and yet, gentle; capable of great delicacy of touch. When I sat on his lap I used to run my fingers over the rough contours of his hands, in the same way that some children suck their thumbs or others have a piece of fabric they rub against their skin. This unconscious action had a hypnotic effect that drew me deeper into the worlds Dadda created with his wonderful storytelling.

And I loved the smell of his pipe tobacco; on his hands or in the wool of his misshapen old cardigan or hanging in the air of the living room. Once in a while I catch a whiff of that same blend of tobacco and I am transported back to the happiest days of my life.

.....

My mother took up smoking after we left Dadda and I have always connected the habit with the gradual fading of her looks.

As I have said, she was an attractive young woman. When I was fourteen, staying for a while with Grandma and Grandpa, I found some photographs of hers and Dadda's wedding day. I remember being surprised at how attractive I thought she was: slim, despite her pregnancy; fine, mousy-blonde hair; and a pretty face, still soft and round like a young girl's. Which is what she was.

They're interesting photographs, taken outside the registry office. The only people with genuine smiles on their faces are Grandma and Grandpa; relief, I should imagine. Dadda looked kind and resigned; my mother looked sullen and bored; her siblings and their families just looked uncomfortable in their best clothes; and Dadda's best man, Big Mick, looked impatient. To get to the reception, judging by what I know about him.

Like many workmen Big Mick smoked roll-ups; he could roll them one-handed and I used to watch, amazed as he turned out perfect cylindrical cigarettes time after time. When I took up smoking dope, many years later, I tried to master the one-handed technique but never managed to get the hang of it. I was never tempted to smoke ordinary cigarettes; unlike my mother who took to them with a vengeance, seeming to start on about twenty a day and increasing her habit over the years. By the time we parted company she must have been getting through over sixty a day.

"I've got to have some pleasure in life," she told me when I suggested one time that she might be smoking too much.

8

I drink a lot, I know that, but I don't crave alcohol. I never drink during the day and I have never let it interfere with my work. I enjoy it, it's as simple as that. It blurs the edges, softens the focus and helps me, usually, to sleep a dreamless sleep.

Unlike most of the other kids at school I didn't start drinking until I was eighteen. Not out of any sense of legality, I just wasn't interested before then. I do remember my first taste of beer though and that was when I was five years old. It was at a party at Grandma and Grandpa's house; I think it might have been Grandpa's fiftieth birthday. It was a Saturday or Sunday afternoon and the house was full of friends and relatives. My mother's sisters and brother were there with their families that, at that time, included six of my cousins.

.....

After my mother and I left the area three more cousins were born. I met them when I lived temporarily with Grandma and Grandpa and once more when I was seventeen, but I never kept in touch with any of them.

I saw most of them again four years ago when they buried Michael, the youngest. He was killed in a car crash at the age of twenty-four. I only realised it was his funeral because Father Courtenay happened to tell me about the accident. As they all gathered around the grave I'd dug I watched them from a distance and tried to identify who was who, but I couldn't even remember most of their names. For a brief, foolish moment I thought my mother might make an appearance but, of course, she didn't. She wouldn't have put herself out for something as inconsequential as a nephew's funeral.

As they filed away towards the cemetery gates they passed close to me, leaning against an old cedar tree. I didn't recognise any of them and certainly didn't expect them to recognise me. As I filled in Michael's grave I wondered if my mother was still in touch with any of them. Or if she was still alive, even.

.....

Most of the kids were running around like lunatics; in and out of Grandpa and Grandma's house and up and down the entry while the adults ate, drank and made merry. There was Irish music playing in the front room and a fairly raucous level of noise throughout the house. At one point things in the kitchen went quiet and I wandered in to find one of my cousins singing a song to an attentive audience of adults. When she finished there was a huge round of applause and a friend of Grandpa's, Uncle Somebody-or-Other, gave her a sixpence. Seeing this I decided I'd like some pocket money as well and spent five minutes or more tugging at Uncle Somebody-or-Other's trouser leg trying to get his attention. Eventually he took notice of me and explained that I'd have to earn my sixpence, at which point Big Mick stepped in.

"So you want to earn a sixpence, do you Mason? Come here," he said, placing me in front of him and holding his glass of beer over my head.

"Now then," he continued, "you punch me as hard as you can in the belly. Right here. And if you make me spill my drink, you can have a tanner."

It was 'catch-22': to get the sixpence I'd also have to get a good soaking. I laughed excitedly as I swung feeble, badly aimed punches at Big Mick's stomach while simultaneously trying to leap backwards out of range of his glass. Suffice it to say I didn't manage to upset his

21

drink although I did scrape my knuckles on his belt buckle on one of my braver attempts. The other adults in the kitchen found the whole thing thoroughly amusing and at the end of it Big Mick took me to one side. He checked first with Dadda that it was OK before telling me I deserved a reward and offering me a sip of his beer. It tasted horrible but I took a good swig and spent the rest of the afternoon trying to coerce other grown-ups into letting me have a taste of their drinks.

My mother hadn't been present at the party while all this was happening; she turned up later with a young man of about her age. I assumed he was just a friend of hers, which he might have been for all I know. Whatever their relationship was, there followed a heated, low volume altercation between Grandpa and my mother, with him making it plain the young man wasn't welcome. My mother argued that other people had brought friends so why shouldn't she be allowed? I overheard that much before one of my aunts took me out of earshot. Shortly afterwards I saw Big Mick having a quiet word with Dadda and steering him towards the front door. I started to follow them but Big Mick sent me back saying he and Dadda were off to the pub for a drink.

"Men's talk, son. You'll get to come with us when you're old enough," he told me.

Before they left, Dadda gave me a weak smile. There was a strange look on his face that I didn't understand and which unsettled me. It was one of only three occasions that I saw him really cut to the quick.

9

When I was growing up on Manning Road there were a lot less cars around and it was a safer place for children to play than it is now.

There were six or seven families near us with kids of about the same age as me and we used to play out together, on the pavement or in the small front gardens. Games like acky-one-two-three; grandmother's footsteps; tig; and Grand National, jumping over the low hedges between the gardens, to the constant annoyance of the hedge owners. Sometimes the girls would draw out a hopscotch track and we'd play that, although I was never much good at it. Other times we'd just sit on someone's front step and chatter away in the way kids do, about nothing in particular.

They were a good bunch and I used to love hanging around with them, being part of a happy sociable gang.

Playing out on the street we always said 'Hello' to passers-by, whether we knew them or not. And people always responded. Things were a lot more polite then.

The gravedigger first appeared about two years before I was taken away from Manning Road. Seeing him wasn't a common occurrence but it was always an occasion when we did. He was a strange, incongruous figure as he loped along on the other side of the road. No matter what the season his appearance never changed: he wore big, black army surplus boots; thick grey woollen trousers; a collarless, lightly striped shirt over a 'granddad' vest; and a huge, thick grey army surplus overcoat. Even on the hottest days of summer he still wore that coat. An old canvas bag, like a gas mask bag, hung from one shoulder and on the other he carried his shovel, the old-fashioned type with a heart-shaped blade and long, straight handle. His hair was blonde and spiky, like a punk's, but this was many years before they arrived on the fashion scene.

Although I never got closer than the road's width away I still have a vivid mental picture of his face: gaunt, chiselled, sallow features with sharp cheekbones and chin; a grim, hard line of a mouth; hawk-like nose; and sunken eyes like points of jet. He moved inexorably along Manning Road keeping his focus straight ahead, never looking aside even when he crossed Farm Road, the side road opposite Dadda's house. It was a wonder he wasn't run over.

We all knew what he did for a living and the neighbourhood was rife with stories and ghoulish speculation about him; as a consequence of which some of the kids ran indoors when he was seen approaching, while others hid behind garden walls and hedges. I don't know why but I was never scared of him. I used to stand out in the open, watching him, hoping he would glance over so I could get a better look into those eyes. But he never did. I thought he looked sad and I felt sorry for him, assuming he was lonely. It never occurred to me that he might want a solitary life and that the invisible barrier he seemed to have erected around himself was a deliberate choice to maintain this solitude.

Whatever his motives or circumstances might have been he remained a total enigma. I never saw anyone speak to him or try to intercept him. He was like a ghost; a notion that was reinforced years later when I asked various people if they remembered him and no one did.

10

I've mentioned the story of my mother at Grandpa's fiftieth birthday party; here are some more stories about her and birthdays:

On my mother's eighteenth birthday Dadda and Grandma arranged a surprise party for her at Dadda's house. She was at work during the day and they organised it so everything was ready and the guests were all in place by the time she was due home at around six thirty.

She usually came in through the back door so at about six twenty-five everyone piled into the front room and they kept a look out for her through the bay window. By six fifty there was no sign of her so her brother drove around to the shop where she worked but he found it shuttered and locked. Time ticked on and most people hung around until about eight thirty before drifting away. Grandma was getting increasingly worried so Grandpa and my uncle checked a couple of the local pubs, still with no luck.

Sometime around ten twenty she arrived home, blind-drunk, threw up over the front steps and continued throwing up throughout the night. She was almost seven months into her pregnancy.

I have heard her tell this story on more than one occasion and to her it's a big joke. Obviously she wasn't to know about the party, so she can't be blamed for that; and, ultimately, there was no harm done because I am here now. I have no idea how ill she felt the next day, nor what Grandma and Grandpa's reaction was. And I can't even begin to imagine the night Dadda must have had, seeing her in that state, listening to her vomiting, terrified she would miscarry, that another child would die before it had a chance to live.

On the evening of my fourteenth birthday I returned from school to an empty home; a second floor maisonette on a grim, unattractive council estate. The post, which never arrived until almost midday, was on the doormat when I came through the door. There was a birthday card from Grandma and Grandpa and, unusually, one from one of my aunts. I'd received no birthday greeting from my mother that morning, let alone a card or present; she'd left for work in a hurry telling me there were things in the fridge for dinner and that she might have a surprise for me when she got home. No one in my class knew it was my birthday as I'd only been attending that particular school for a few months, so it was like any other day for me.

Sometime after nine o'clock my mother arrived home with her boyfriend, Andy. She had been drinking and was very excitable, but she wasn't drunk. She told me that Andy had just been offered a two-year contract working in Saudi Arabia and she was going to go with him. She'd been in touch with Grandma and Grandpa and they were happy for me stay with them while she and Andy settled in. She said it would only be for a few months and then I'd be able to join them out there. She went on and on about how exciting it all was and how she couldn't wait. It was Andy who noticed the cards on top of the television.

"When was it your birthday, Mace?" he asked.

My mother looked around, confused, and took the card he was holding.

"When did this come?" she asked.

"Today," I told her.

"But it's not your birthday today is it?"

When I said it was I couldn't help but notice the look on Andy's face, a mixture of embarrassment and disgust. He couldn't believe she'd forgotten her own son's birthday. He didn't know her that well then.

On my eighteenth birthday my friends, Patrick and Howie, took me for my first proper drink. I had three pints of beer - which I didn't really enjoy – and I was a bit tipsy when I got home, accompanied by Howie who came in for coffee. We were in the living room, listening to music when my mother came home with her friend Brenda, a divorcee grandmother in her late thirties who lived next door.

"Here he is, Bren. Here's my son, the birthday boy. The man!" my mother crowed as they sailed into the room on a wave of alcohol fumes and cigarette smoke.

"Happy birthday, Macey," Brenda shrilled, throwing her arms around my neck and spilling my coffee. "Where have you been, then?"

When I said we'd been to the pub my mother pushed her face into mine to smell my breath.

"He's been drinking, Bren! My boy! He's never had a drink in his life!"

"He's turning into a real man overnight," shrieked Brenda.

"No, Bren, not a real man, if you know what I mean. Not a real man!"

They found this incredibly funny and, laughing hysterically, went into the kitchen so I could be alone with my 'friend', as my mother referred pointedly to Howie. He was obviously embarrassed and soon made his excuses and left.

On my way to bed I went to get a glass of water from the kitchen where my mother and Brenda were drinking gin. They invited me to join them but I said I'd had enough to drink. As I said 'goodnight' my mother gave me a sloppy birthday kiss on the cheek. (The only times she showed me any kind of affection were when she was drunk.)

"Oh, come on!" cried Brenda. "He's a grown man now. He needs a proper kiss."

With which she grabbed me and kissed me long and hard on the mouth, even trying to force her tongue between my lips. I managed to fight her off and left the two of them shrieking like banshees as I escaped to my bedroom. Or rather: I thought I'd escaped.

As I lay in bed, trying to stop the room spinning, I could hear them chattering away downstairs in the kitchen, their volume rising and falling. At one point one of them came upstairs to use the toilet but after that things seemed to quieten down and I was just starting to doze off when my bedroom door suddenly flew open and Brenda burst in.

"Mason," she announced, "your mother's asked me to make a man of you. It's a joint birthday present from the both of us."

She pulled off her sweater, revealing her ample, bra-clad breasts as she advanced towards me and sat on my bed. Leaning over me so that her breasts almost spilled out of the cups of her bra, she started running her fingers through my hair, down my neck and under the blankets onto my torso. Terrified, I pulled the blankets up to my chin and told her to stop but she ignored me, pressing herself against my body, smothering my face with kisses, searching for my mouth with her fleshy lips and tongue. I was concentrating so much on keeping her mouth away from mine that I didn't notice her hand had slipped under the covers. Before I knew what was happening she thrust inside my underpants, grabbed my penis and started tugging at it violently. I kicked and lashed out with all my strength, knocking her off the bed before I pulled the blankets around me and curled up, foetus-like, with my pillow clutched in front of me. She lay on the floor for a minute, stunned and winded, until she got her breath back and started cackling in that rasping, alcohol-soaked, nicotine-coarse laugh of hers. Wheezing and coughing she got to her feet, collected her top and made for the door where she stopped and turned. One of the bra straps had slipped off her shoulder and a big brown nipple was exposed on one of her mountainous, blue-veined, pallid white breasts.

"If you change your mind, Macey, I'm just downstairs. Or right next door if you want to leave it 'til another night."

She hooked her strap back into place with her thumb, winked at me, closed the door behind her and slapped her way downstairs, where her drain laughter was joined by my mother's.

I'd like to think it was a joke but, while there was an element of humour in her behaviour, I'm sure she would have gone through with it if I'd given in to her. And my mother would have let her.

On my fifteenth birthday my mother had not long returned from Saudi Arabia and I had been moved again, this time from my grandparents' house. My mother found it difficult living with them, unable to cope with Grandma watching over her, commenting on her behaviour, acting as a moral barometer.

At the time of my birthday she didn't have a boyfriend and Brenda hadn't moved in next door yet, so it was just the two of us for a change.

She gave me a card at the breakfast table. My grandparents' card had arrived the day before, so I suppose she'd had a bit of warning.

"I'll give you your present later," she told me as she stubbed out a cigarette before snatching up her bag and rushing out to work.

I was struggling with some physics homework when she arrived home that evening, carrying a large bag of fish and chips.

"Thought we'd have a treat," she said, putting them on the kitchen table.

And it was a treat. I liked fish and chips; especially in preference to my mother's cooking.

"Pop them in the oven for a minute and lay the table. I've just got to nip upstairs."

I did as she asked and had everything ready when she came back into the kitchen with a hastily wrapped present.

"Here you are, Mason. I hope it's right."

I could tell it was a book, but I had no idea what kind of book to expect. I unwrapped it slowly to find the photography book; a really good book. I was amazed. I didn't think she knew I was interested in photography, beyond the fact that I had a camera. I stared at it blankly for a few seconds.

"Is it right?" she asked anxiously. "The man in the shop said it was a good one."

"Yes, it's... It's really good."

I was at a loss. I almost wanted to hug her but couldn't quite bring myself to do so. I sensed she was having the same struggle but, without a drink inside her, physical contact between us was going to be unlikely. I gave her a big, genuine smile and flicked through the pages. We were saved further awkwardness by the smell of the chip paper browning in the oven.

"Oh, my God! The chips!" she flustered.

I continued flicking through the book while she took the chips out of the oven and put them onto plates. I wasn't quite sure how to adequately express myself and I watched her for a moment, clutching the book to my chest.

"Thanks," I said to her back. "It really is really good."

She stopped dividing up the food and stood motionless at the kitchen unit.

"Good," she replied without looking around. And I saw the tension leave her body, like a weight had been lifted from her shoulders. She turned with the plates and, handing one to me, wished me a happy birthday.

11

These days I don't bother celebrating my birthday. Tom once tried to find out when it was but I wouldn't tell him.

"Why do you want to know?" I asked.

"You know mine," he replied.

"So?"

"I'd like to get you a card or something. We could celebrate."

"Celebrate how?"

"I don't know. Have a few drinks or something."

"What are we doing now?"

"But it'd be different."

"How would it be different?"

He thought about this for a moment.

"Oh, forget it! You're a miserable sod," he told me.

"I do my best," I replied.

.....

The last time I celebrated Dadda's birthday with him Grandpa took me to the local newsagents and gave me a few pennies to buy pipe cleaners and spills for him as a present. He always kept a ready supply in a lathe-turned wooden container that stood on a corner of the tiled mantelpiece in the living room.

I can visualise that setting clearly: the blackened fire irons and brass coal scuttle; the ornaments and clock on the mantel; the landscape painting on the chimney breast; the chairs either side of the hearth, Dadda's handmade rocker chair opposite a comfy old armchair.

I used to love the ritual of lighting the fire. While Dadda swept out the ashes and crumbling, grey cinders I'd twist the pages of old magazines and papers into fire lighters which he'd lay in the grate with kindling and a few lumps of coal. Then he'd put a match to it all and hold a full sheet of newspaper over the mouth of the fireplace to get it to draw. I'd watch anxiously as the paper yellowed, then browned, sucked in as the flames licked higher and the draught roared louder, until there was an explosion of burning sparks that flew up the chimney. I always worried Dadda would get burned but he never did. Then we'd sit in his rocking chair, basking in the heat as we watched the embers glow and the flames dance.

"You can't beat a good blaze," Dadda used to say.

I imagine it was next to that hearth that Grandpa poured out his heart to Dadda about my mother's pregnancy, the two men nursing glasses of whisky, Dadda sucking contemplatively on his pipe.

On that last birthday with Dadda, my mother, despite the fact that she worked in the city centre where she had access to a variety of shops to choose from, gave him a packet of tobacco, a present that required absolutely no effort or imagination. She didn't even wrap it. After all he had given up and done for her that was the extent of her gratitude. Of course Dadda expressed nothing less than delight in his gift; he would not have been so graceless as to react otherwise.

My mother had good cause to express delight in the presents she received from Dadda because he always put a lot of thought into them.

When I was eleven my mother and her boyfriend, Danny, gave me a pair of football boots for Christmas, despite the fact that I had no interest in football. This was typical of the presents I got from my mother over the years, which was why the photography book was all the more surprising.

.....

I remember two things about the newsagent: he wore an emerald-green eye-patch over one eye and he would only give deposits on empty pop bottles that had been bought in his shop. When I went back to live with Grandma and Grandpa, while my mother was in the Middle East, I asked them about him. They told me he had died several years ago but it was true about the deposits. He had some way of telling if the bottle had come from his shop but no one ever found out how he did it. People bought bottles of pop from him and examined them when they got home, comparing them to identical bottles from other shops, but they never discovered his secret.

"He was a terrible old skinflint," said Grandma. "He wouldn't give you the drippings off his nose."

.....

"I could get you a present," said Tom a while later, trying again.

"What if I didn't like it?" I asked.

"You could pretend, couldn't you?"

"I'm no good at pretending," I told him.

"You could give it back then," he replied.

"Then I'd feel guilty and embarrassed."

"I won't give you a present then. I'll just give you a card!"

"What if I didn't like the card?"

"Don't worry, I'll give you one I know you'll like."

"How would you know?"

"It'd be plain black. Get the drinks in."

12

I have always had a strong work ethic, believing in doing my best and giving good value. I probably earned my pocket money more than most kids do, taking on a lot of the responsibility for the upkeep of the various households I shared with my mother. Not that I minded. I was quite happy doing jobs around the home. It filled the time and I took a lot of satisfaction from a job well done. I still do.

.....

I started earning money, other than pocket money, when I was living with Grandma and Grandpa. I was fourteen at the time. Since then, apart from the periods when I was travelling, I have always had some kind of job, either part-time or full-time.

That first job was cleaning windows.

Grandpa's health had started to deteriorate in the seven years since my mother and I left Manning Road; he wasn't always his old energetic self any more. So one Saturday when he didn't feel up to doing the windows Grandma asked if I thought I could do them. I said I thought I could and she sent me around to a neighbour's house to ask if I could borrow his ladders.

Desie Nugent and his young family had moved in, seven doors down, a couple of years earlier. He was a small, freckly, friendly man with sandy-brown hair and a tough wiry physique. He took the time to show me how to lift his extendable aluminium ladders, how to get them balanced properly for carrying and how to foot and raise them. On that first occasion he even carried them around to Grandma and Grandpa's house for me.

When I'd finished Grandma's house, which took some time as I was meticulous about not leaving any runs or smears, I returned the ladders to Desie, who asked what I'd charge to do his windows. As I wasn't getting anything for doing Grandma's windows I had no idea, so he offered me fifty pence, a small fortune to a fourteen-year-old. Then, while I was cleaning Desie's windows, his neighbour Mrs. Astley asked if I could do hers and by the end of the day I'd done six houses, earning a total of two pounds fifty, with requests to return in a fortnight. Eventually I was cleaning the windows of eleven houses along Manning Road, a task which took all day every other Saturday but earned me five pounds a fortnight, most of which went into a post office savings account I opened.

Grandma wasn't particularly happy about my new job because it meant I had less time to do errands for her; I noticed that she stopped giving me pocket money, which should have been taken out of the money my mother sent. Grandma also insisted that I clean Desie's windows for free as I was using his ladders but Desie wouldn't hear of it. He gave me my fifty pence and told me to keep quiet about it if Grandma asked. On hot days his wife, Fidelma, used to offer me a bottle of beer as well, but I always refused politely, accepting a glass of pop instead.

It was a good time for me. I was doing a proper job to earn my own money and I was being treated like an adult. For the first time I started to feel like a young man rather than a boy.

It was a feeling that would soon be knocked out of me.

.....

The only part of the job I didn't like was cleaning the windows of Dadda's old house, then occupied by the Morgan family. Things had changed. The front was the same but at the back a single storey extension had been built which housed a new bathroom, making space for a third bedroom upstairs. The extension occupied what used to be the paved area below the lawn, which now looked terribly neglected - uncut and scrubby with several bare patches. Dadda's flowerbeds had been decimated; trampled and torn by the Morgans' three children and their yappy little terrier. The shed - once an ordered workshop but now used as an external junk room - was in need of a coat of paint, as was all of the exterior woodwork of the house. And the fence running next to the entry had planks missing and broken all along its length.

I found it very unsettling looking in through the windows at the rooms I had grown up in. Different decor. Different furniture. Different atmosphere. Where once it had been kept scrupulously clean and tidy there was clutter and mess. The pleasant aroma of Dadda's pipe had been replaced by an unpleasant stink, a combination of soiled nappies, strong disinfectant and what I can only describe as a watery cabbage smell. It made me feel physically sick. I saw it as a desecration of Dadda's memory.

Of all the houses whose windows I cleaned, that was the only one I ever rushed, a fact I felt guilty about. It wasn't very fair on the Morgans and I hope they never realised they were being short-changed - it wasn't their fault, after all - I just wasn't comfortable being around there any more.

I have a solid work ethic but it's nothing to do with 'the Protestant work ethic'. I don't toil in the hope of a reward in some afterlife. I work hard because it gives me satisfaction and because it's what I think is good and right.

13

From the ages of eighteen to twenty-eight I lived an unsettled life, moving from job to job, never staying in one place for more than eight or nine months, earning and saving enough money to pay for a three or four-month trip to mainland Europe where I'd hitchhike, camp and generally bum around.

Tom envied me that I made those trips; that, as he put it, I refused to fit into a mould or a pigeonhole; that I did my own thing. I explained to him that I wasn't doing my own thing; I was doing what lots of young people were doing then and are still doing today, each for their own reasons. The only difference with me was that I didn't know what my reasons were and, ultimately, I got nothing out of the trips.

"But you must have been enriched by the experiences you had," Tom insisted.

"What experiences?" I asked bluntly.

"Well, what did you do while you were there?"

So I told him. For much of the time I was too drunk or stoned to know or care where I was or what I was doing. I wasn't interested in doing the usual cultural or tourist stuff in places like Rome or Paris. In fact I visited very few towns or cities; and if I did I found myself drawn to out-of-the-way, indigenously populated areas where I would sit anonymously in bars and cafés, watching life go by. More often than not I'd avoid urban areas, happier staying for days on end in a field on the outskirts of some remote village, content to drink cheap wine, smoke marijuana and watch the cows and the clouds and the wind in the trees.

"Do you know why I went abroad?" I asked Tom. "Because when I was there I had no responsibilities and because it was cheap. I could get drunk cheaply. Living in a tent was cheaper than renting a room. Hitchhiking was cheaper than trains or planes or coaches. And if I didn't feel like doing anything or talking to anyone I didn't have to."

.....

Throughout those ten years the work I did was almost always unskilled labour. It wasn't always possible to find regular jobs but I could usually get something through a temping agency. The pay wasn't as good but I didn't care as long as I could eat, drink, cover my rent (when necessary) and put some money aside.

In one respect the temping jobs were better because I wasn't expected to mix with the other workers; to sit with them in canteens on breaks or join in with their card games and banter. Most of the people I worked with were OK and left me to myself, apart from the odd pleasantry, but occasionally there would be one or two who insisted on trying to involve me. Probably so they could make fun of me openly instead of in whispers behind my back. I was 'the loner'; 'the outsider'; 'the weirdo'. Generally speaking I didn't mind; they could make jokes about me as long as I was left alone. There were a couple of occasions when I was goaded to the point where I almost reacted, but I managed to contain myself.

.....

I only ever snapped once, during a rainy lunchtime at school when I was sixteen.

I had been feeling ill all morning and when the bell went for lunch I asked our form teacher, Mr. Trewick, if I could go home. Mr. Trewick was a small, slope-shouldered, bearded, insecure man who was scared of the bigger, tougher boys in the school. He compensated for this by meting out slipperings and detentions to the rest of us and by wielding his authority in a mean, arbitrary fashion. Telling me there was nothing wrong with me and denying me permission to go home was a typical example.

As usual we were unsupervised during the lunch period, apart from the occasional peek around the door from the teacher on duty. Towards the end of break a game of piggy-in-the-middle started up in class, with several of the boys throwing one of the girls' bags around the room. It was all good-natured fun but got more and more hectic, with the girl screaming and screeching and the boys getting louder and wilder. As I sat, slumped against a radiator, trying to get some sleep amidst all the horseplay, their shrieks and shouts knifed through my head, which was already pounding. In the end it got to be too much and I decided I had to get out of the room. But as I started to rise from my chair one of the boys, Corbin, mis-aimed his throw and the girl's bag hit me in the face with considerable force, banging the back of my head against the radiator. It was almost certainly an accident.

Corbin was an ordinary kid, neither a tough guy nor a weed. He was an inch or two shorter than me but broader, more heavy set; a good sportsman and probably quite strong. To be honest it wouldn't have made any difference who he was because I went blank.

I opened my eyes and, through a blur of tears, saw him laughing as he apologised and asked for the bag back. Without thinking, I stood up, grabbed his tie and propelled him the length of the classroom, thudding him into the back wall. I pressed my face close to his, tightened my grip and told him that if he ever did anything like that again I would kill him. I remember he looked surprised and scared and made no attempt to fight, or answer, back. I carried on twisting his tie into his throat until his face turned crimson and he started choking, at which point I let him go.

And I thought that that was that. I'd made my point and I turned away intending to sit down again. But as I got halfway down the room a jag of pain shot through my head and, without knowing what I was doing, my hand curled around the back of a chair and I swung it over my shoulder, hurling it at Corbin, who was still at the back of the room. It missed his head by inches and hit the wall with such force that two of the legs smashed on impact.

The room was silent. No one moved or said a thing but it was more of a shock to me than it was to anyone else. I was overwhelmed by a wave of nausea that left me shaking and on the verge of tears.

Not wanting to break down in front of everyone I snatched up my bag and ran out of the classroom and straight out of school.

The next day I was called into the deputy headmaster's office to explain my actions and subsequent disappearance. I told him what had happened and blamed Mr. Trewick, saying it wouldn't have happened if I'd been allowed to go home. I was dismissed with a mild reprimand. According to rumour Mr. Trewick didn't get off so lightly.

.....

The incident with Corbin changed my usual 'misfit' reputation in school. I'm not sure quite what my new reputation was, but there was a marked difference; I noticed that I was given an even wider berth than usual and I was sometimes the subject of whispered comments and conversations. Secretly, I quite liked that.

14

I never went away on holiday with Dadda, probably because my mother didn't like the idea of going somewhere as a family for a whole week. The truth is she was embarrassed to be seen with Dadda; they never went out together socially, apart from family occasions. Instead of long holidays we took day trips, which she came on occasionally, depending on her mood and where we were going. Usually we drove into the surrounding countryside and had a picnic or visited some small stately home or place of historical interest.

My mother wasn't much interested in history or doing anything active. As soon as we arrived at our destination she would find a spot, not too far from the car, where she'd settle down on her own, happily reading magazines or sleeping in the sun.

I wasn't particularly keen on old houses and suchlike either. My favourite pastime was walking through woodland, with Dadda pointing out the different types of trees, showing me how to identify them by the shape of their leaves and their bark. He'd tell me the best uses for the wood of each of the trees and we'd hunt for interesting roots or bits of fallen branches that he could take home to work with. When we found a piece we liked we'd take turns examining it, wondering what it might evolve into in Dadda's skilful hands. He always said he'd teach me to whittle when I got old enough to handle sharp knives.

Another vivid memory from my childhood is of Dadda and me sitting on a carpet of soft, fine grass in a copse of young oaks that covered a small hill. There were tiny, star-shaped white flowers dotted around us and a gentle breeze stirred the branches of the trees, creating mottled patterns of sunlight that shifted and shimmered on the grass. Dadda was holding a lump of dead bough and telling me a fabulous story about a dragon, the guardian of a great treasure, who lay asleep under the knoll beneath us. In hundreds of years' time the roots of the oaks would reach down, deep enough to stir the dragon from its slumbers and it would awake. Then it would share out the treasure among the poor people of the world and carry off the evil men who oppressed them, dumping them on a hidden island in the middle of a secret ocean. (Although we never spoke about politics I suspect Dadda was a socialist.)

When I asked Dadda how he knew about the dragon he said he could sense it by holding the wood. I asked if I could sense it too. He said he saw no reason why not and passed it to me. After several minutes I'd felt nothing unusual and scrutinised the wood for signs of the dragon but saw only a dried-out piece of dead tree.

.....

I believe Dadda did find inspiration through handling wood rather than just looking at it. I think he was genuinely in touch with nature and receptive to its energies. Over the years I have tried to discover the same sensitivity but with no real success; but I have learned to enjoy the feel of natural things for their own sake.

.....

A couple of months later the dragon emerged; a long thin scaly creature with a forked tail curling around its hindquarters. It was a beautiful piece, about nine or ten inches long with a ridge of spines along its back and a fierce face with flared nostrils. I always thought of it as a companion piece to my castle: they had the same style and seemed to belong to the same story in the same world.

.....

If we didn't go out on a day trip in the holidays Dadda always did something to make the day special. In the way that Sundays were special.

I liked Sundays. We'd get up early and while my mother and I got ready for church Dadda prepared something light for us to eat; cereal or toast. My mother usually went out on Friday and Saturday evenings and didn't always make it home on Friday nights, but she was always in the house on a Sunday morning. While she and I went to nine o'clock mass with Grandma and Grandpa, Dadda prepared the Sunday dinner. Then he'd cook a big fry-up of bacon, eggs, sausages, beans and fried bread, which would be ready and waiting for us when we got back from church. After breakfast I'd help him do the dishes and he'd spend a bit of time with me before going to the pub to meet Grandpa and their friends for a lunchtime pint. While he was gone Grandma usually came around to make sure my mother wasn't ruining the dinner and I'd play out on the street with whoever was around. When Dadda got back we'd sit down to a full roast dinner after which we'd tidy up and have a rest before going into the garden or out to the park. Or, if the weather was bad, I'd curl up on Dadda's lap while he smoked his pipe and we'd watch a film on TV, in front of which my mother would inevitably fall asleep. Sunday tea was sandwiches, cake, tinned fruit, condensed milk and, sometimes, trifle, which my mother got quite good at making under Grandma's tuition. After tea Dadda would give me a bath before tucking me up in bed with a story.

Sundays: special days, with special meals and lots of quality time with Dadda.

Saturdays were good days too, although the food wasn't quite so lavish; maybe boiled eggs for breakfast instead of cereal and a treat at lunchtime, like sausages and fried onions in a soft bread roll, just like from a hot dog stall, only better. I probably spent less time with Dadda and more time playing out on the street on Saturdays, but just knowing he was somewhere close by always gave me a warm, comforting feeling.

On weekdays Dadda had already left for work by the time my mother got me up and I'd only see him for an hour or so after he got home before it was my bedtime. But during the holidays he was the one who woke me up and we'd spend all day together until he put me back to bed, tired and happy, in the evening. I loved those days.

.....

When the weather was too bad to go outside a favourite indoor game was hide and seek; although we never played it when my mother was at home. Dadda would close his eyes and count to fifty while I ran around the house looking for a 'hidey-hole', favourite places being: the cupboard under the stairs; the built-in wardrobe in our bedroom, which had the trap door up to the loft in its ceiling; behind the big, plump settee in the front room; under the table in the front room, where I was hidden by the floor-length table cloth. I still remember the quiver of expectation when I heard Dadda shout: "Fifty! Here I come Mason, ready or not." Then there was the wait. He'd rarely come straight into the room I was hiding in or, if he did, he'd make a big show of not being able to find me before moving on to another room. There were many times when the anticipation of being found became too intense, bordering on panic and I'd burst out of my hiding place, unable to contain myself, laughing hysterically and jumping about with relief.

When it was Dadda's turn to hide I would invariably cheat, counting too quickly or inaccurately before calling out: "Here I come Dadda, ready or not." More often than not he'd help me locate him if I was having difficulty - a cough or the movement of a curtain - and when I'd found him he always expressed disbelief, telling me he was sure I'd never be able to find him so quickly.

There was only one occasion when the game went wrong. Dadda was hiding and, try as I might, I couldn't find him anywhere, despite searching every room twice. I knew he wouldn't leave me alone in the house and I started getting scared, convinced that he had vanished somehow. I ran from room to room, calling for him more and more desperately, unable to understand where he had disappeared to. Eventually I heard him calling and as I ran into our bedroom he appeared from the built-in wardrobe. For a joke he'd climbed up into the loft but, as he waited in silence, he'd heard water dripping and become distracted as he searched for the leak. He apologised and promised never to do it again.

We didn't play hide and seek for a while after that.

.....

Another 'joke' that backfired was due to my mother.

The park Dadda usually took me to was within walking distance of Manning Road but there was another, much larger one we used to go to, a good twenty minutes' drive away. This park, situated on the outskirts of town, contained lakes, woods and areas of heath. It also had a fantastic playground, with the usual swings, slides and roundabouts but also climbing frames, a witch's hat and one enormous slide that seemed to be taller than the trees. When I went with Dadda I was usually allowed to play for as long as I liked, running from one apparatus to the next, hungry for more thrills.

On the occasion in question – a crisp, clear, chilly day – my mother had accompanied us, which was most unusual. However, she obviously got bored or cold quite quickly and, after what seemed a very short period of time, she decided she wanted to leave and called me to get off the big red roundabout. Some older boys were pushing it, spinning it really fast and I had no intention of getting off. It was like flying.

When I showed no sign of heeding her she called again.

"Mason! We're going! Come on, now! If you don't come now we're going without you!"

I heard but I still ignored her, whooping and waving at Dadda as I hurtled around. I was having a great time.

As the roundabout began to slow down I saw her dragging Dadda towards the car. I wasn't particularly worried at this stage but as they got into the car the boys started pushing again and the speed picked up. I was more concerned when I saw the car shudder and fumes billow out of the exhaust.

They wouldn't...

The car reversed out of its parking space and my mother leant out of the passenger window, waving and yelling:

"Bye Mason," in a taunting, singsong voice.

But there was nothing I could do; the roundabout was moving faster and faster as Dadda's car pulled out of the car park onto the driveway.

"Dadda!"

He can't have heard me.

"DADDA!"

The boys were still pushing and everything was speeding up, including Dadda's car as it headed towards the park gate. I remember the feeling of terror as I realised I wouldn't be able to find my way home. And it was all getting faster and the car was near the gate and the boys were laughing at me screaming out for my Dadda and the adults sitting nearby didn't seem to care and I was getting desperate and it got so fast, everything...

"DADDA!"

And I leapt off the roundabout, tearing my knees, elbows, hands and face as I hit the gravely concrete before clambering to my feet to chase the disappearing car.

The cuts and grazes soon healed but for years afterwards I had nightmares in which I was abandoned and lost.

I never blamed Dadda for what happened; he would never have done anything like that. He comforted and reassured me at the time and, afterwards, whenever I woke crying from the bad dreams. My mother showed no remorse nor offered any solace; all she had to say was that it was my fault for not coming when she called me.

.....

One day in the holidays, when the weather wasn't up to a run out

42

in the countryside, Dadda took me for my first trip to the cinema. I was used to watching our black-and-white television but that was no preparation for the experience of seeing Walt Disney's *Fantasia* on the big screen, in technicolour, with a cinema sound system; an explosion of brilliant images and thumping music. I must have been five or six at the time and I sat slack-jawed and wide-eyed through the whole film. Dadda had to keep reminding me to eat my ice cream that was melting, dribbling down my hand and dripping onto my shorts and tee shirt.

Back then the auditorium wasn't cleared after each screening as it is now and it was possible to stay in the cinema for more than one showing of a film. Which is what we did. After two helpings of the Magician's Apprentice and the fairies sprinkling stardust and the dancing hippos and all that other wonderful animation I left the cinema bubbling with excitement.

After that, when he had time, Dadda took me to the Saturday morning cinema club at the local ABC picture house. There were cartoons, serials, a main feature and the ABC Club song that all the kids sang at the tops of their voices. My mother never came with us, although she liked going to the cinema too; but not to see the type of films Dadda and I liked. She went with her friends to see love stories and thrillers and to drool over matinee idols. She'd tell me how handsome and romantic this or that actor was or how exciting such and such a film had been, but I found it hard to understand her enthusiasm. It all sounded boring and lacking in magic. That was the great thing about Dadda's stories and the films he took me to see: they were full of magic.

I only once went to see a film with my mother, when I was about nine years old. We were shopping in the town centre when it started to rain. We had time to kill before meeting her boyfriend, Danny, who had gone to watch a football match, so we ducked into a cinema. We didn't know anything about the movie that was showing but she bought tickets anyway and we sneaked in a couple of minutes after it had started. The film was *Kes*. I was used to seeing bright, funny cartoons or episodes of *Flash Gordon* or exciting films where children and animals did heroic deeds. I thought the bit of *Kes* that we sat through was bleak, depressing and dull, like watching real life. That wasn't why I liked going to the cinema. Fortunately my mother was equally disenchanted. We stayed for about twenty minutes before she tempted me out (unnecessarily) with the promise of orange pop and a cream cake at a teahouse.

.....

I retained a love of the cinema as I grew up and, unlike my religious beliefs, my taste in films became more catholic. I even quite liked *Kes* when I saw it in its entirety many years after that first aborted viewing. However my favourite genres are fantasy and science fiction, the natural progression from Dadda's fantastic stories and the types of books I most enjoyed reading as a boy.

Despite my interest in photography I never had any desire to understand the film-making process; the role of the director or the ways in which the camera is used. I would find no enjoyment in analysing the technical aspects of movie production. For me the illusion is everything and I have no interest in understanding the nuts and bolts of creating that illusion.

These days I rarely go to the cinema as I find myself constantly irritated by the munching of popcorn, the rustle of sweet papers and the whisperings of people who lack the imagination to immerse themselves in the story on the screen. Knowing my preference for sci-fi and fantasy Tom used to tip me off if there was a film coming on he thought I'd like. I'd sometimes make the effort to see it, usually at an off-peak showing when there would be less people and, hopefully, less sources of irritation. In general though I rely on the small screen to provide my cinematic escapism.

Possibly my favourite film is *Silent Running* starring Bruce Dern. It's a nineteen seventies sci-fi film in which he plays a naturalist on one of a fleet of spaceships. Each of the ships are carrying huge domes with samples of Earth's flora and fauna because our world has become so polluted it is no longer able to sustain many of its life forms. When the order comes to destroy the domes and his three shipmates proceed to blow up all but one of the domes on their ship, Dern's character goes mad. He kills his shipmates, none of whom had any interest in their precious cargo, and he shoots off into outer space, away from the rest of the fleet. For the remainder of the film he is alone apart from two 'droid' robots that take on almost human traits and emotions. With their help he tends to the plants and animals until the fleet miraculously locate him and he realises he will be forced to blow up the last remaining dome. At the end of the film he programmes one of the 'droids' to carry on sustaining life in the dome and blasts it out into space before blowing up the main body of the ship, with himself on board.

I have seen the film several times over the years and always felt a strong empathy with Bruce Dern's character, the loner who no one tried to understand, but I wished he'd sent both droids up with the dome. The one he blows up with himself was damaged and not able to function properly but, even so, I always felt sorry for the one who was left on his own, cut adrift in space.

PART TWO

1

I was born in the front bedroom of Dadda's house on a balmy autumn evening at the start of the nineteen sixties. In the room with my mother were Grandma and the midwife, Pauline Slattery. Downstairs in the living room were Dadda, who I imagine sitting in his rocking chair, calmly smoking his pipe, and Grandpa, hunched in the armchair opposite, a whisky at his elbow, wringing his hands and puffing nervously on roll-ups.

After the birth Grandpa tried to tempt Dadda to the pub for a celebratory drink but Dadda said he'd stay at home in case he was needed. He gave Grandpa some money to get a round of drinks in and insisted that he took Pauline Slattery with him, telling him to buy her anything she wanted.

I was either seven pounds, two ounces or seven pounds, five ounces; I can never remember which. I know it's one or the other. My birth sign is Libra, which I share with Dadda. I'm pretty sceptical about astrology but I suppose it's true to say we were both fairly easy-going, well-balanced people. I don't know much about the 'nature versus nurture' argument but I certainly didn't get my temperament from my mother. Maybe it came from my biological father but I like to think it's something I picked up from Dadda.

I was a healthy baby, growing at a normal rate, developing in all the right ways at all the right times. I got chicken-pox and measles, as most kids did, and bore them and any other illnesses with relatively little fuss. Grandma used to tell me I was the most good-natured and well-behaved of all her grandchildren. The fact that she was heavily involved in my upbringing might have had something to do with that opinion. However I know some of my cousins were real tearaways and had several scrapes with the law when they were growing up. For instance, Michael had a history of joyriding in stolen cars before he died in one.

.....

My first word was "Anma", which is hardly surprising since I spent most of my pre-school time with my grandmother. She was a hard-working, formidable, battleship of a woman. A housewife who spent her days shopping, washing, ironing, cooking and cleaning both her own house and Dadda's; all this while looking after me at the same time. Like most working-class women of that era she was zealously house proud and she went about her chores with good-humoured vigour. There's no doubt that Grandpa wore the trousers in their household but watching Grandma pounding clothes on a washboard, or wringing them through the wringer, or scrubbing the cardinal-red painted front steps, it was plain to see why few people ever crossed her. Even Grandpa. She was a tremendous sight blustering down the street if something or someone got her hackles raised. And she was quite happy to ruffle a few feathers if she felt she had good cause. Not that she always did have good cause, but that never stopped her. On more than one occasion I was dragged, trailing in her wake, as she set off to deal with some reported slight against the family.

"What's this Mary MacIllaney's been saying about our Tommy? I'll soon put a stop to her big gob."

And off she'd sail in high dudgeon while I sprinted alongside on little legs, clinging to her hand and trying to keep up with her.

As I got older she was not averse to giving me the odd smack across the back of the legs if I misbehaved but, generally speaking, she treated me with love and affection. I think she took pride in showing me off when we were out shopping, or walking in the park, or sitting on the gleaming front steps of her house.

.....

It wasn't until I was well into my teens that I discovered Dadda used to give Grandma money to look after me and to help out in our house.

I was complaining to my mother about her lack of generosity and I used Grandma as a shining example; how she had taken on child-minding responsibilities so my mother could work and earn money, which she only ever spent on herself. My mother laughed and told me the facts.

"If your Grandma saw a chance to earn a few quid she'd sell her own mother to the slave trade. She's got more money than any of us, saved up and hidden away. And if your Dadda was soft enough and stupid enough to offer her money then that's his look-out."

At first I refused to believe her. Then I remembered Grandma withholding my pocket money when I was fourteen.

"It should have been you that paid her, then. Not Dadda!" I told her.

"Pay my own mother? Why should I when your Dadda was fool enough to give her money? Anyway, he only encouraged her; she probably would have done it for nothing. We'd never have heard the end of it, but she'd have done it."

.....

Grandma always seemed to be in excellent health. It was almost like she didn't have time to be ill; working and worrying about her family. She never seemed to stop.

"Always on the go," as she used to say.

There were only two occasions that I saw her show any kind of weakness, physical or emotional: when my mother took me away from Dadda and at Grandpa's funeral. He may have worn the trousers but she was the rock that family was built on.

.....

Grandpa was a typical working man who laboured all day and expected his dinner to be on the table when he got home; which it always was. He was a big man; a bricklayer who was responsible for building some of the extensions that appeared in the back gardens of Manning Road. I saw him at work once, building a wall for a neighbour. Despite chatting and joking with me and the teenage lad he employed to mix his mortar and carry his bricks, he threw up the wall in no time. I'm sure he could have built a wall quicker than many men could knock one down.

At parties he was always the first to start up a song and the last to leave. Unless the party was in his own house, in which case Grandma would pack him off to bed so she could clear up.

"She's a great woman your Grandma," he'd say to me. "If only your mother took after her…"

He obviously loved and respected Grandma and took great delight in hearing stories of her run-ins with neighbours or shopkeepers or the establishment.

"Good for you, Grandma," he'd say and turn to me. "Who needs a big dog, Mason, when we've got your grandmother looking after us?"

"Who are you calling a dog?!" she'd shout and chase him playfully around the garden, brandishing a frying pan while I ran behind laughing and shouting encouragement to them both.

…..

Dadda's dinner was rarely ever waiting for him when he got home. Despite the fact that my mother usually got in before him, he did most of the cooking.

Sitting by the fire in the living room one evening, when my mother was out, Big Mick said he thought this was a sad state of affairs. Dadda replied that he had cooked for himself when he lived on his own, so what was the difference? And my mother worked too, so why should she be expected to do it?

"It's the woman's job," Big Mick said.

"Times are changing," Dadda told him. "She's a different generation to us, Mick. Anyway, what would you rather do? Cook it yourself or let someone who can't even boil an egg do it for you?"

They had a good laugh about that.

"You've got a point there, Stephen."

"There you are then," said Dadda.

"I still think you're too soft on her, though."

Dadda smiled and ruffled my hair and changed the subject.

…..

Like most men Grandpa hated to show any sign of weakness and, while he could talk the hind legs off a donkey, I suspect he rarely shared his problems or worries. It was a miracle, then, that he told Dadda about my mother's pregnancy; he must have been at his wits' end. Then again, he'd probably had a few drinks and knew Dadda was a dependable, trustworthy confidant who wouldn't betray him. It would have been a disaster if word had got out.

The good name of their family was paramount to my grandparents and they were fiercely protective of their children and grandchildren. If allegations were made they would deny them or find some mitigating circumstance to explain or condone the alleged behaviour. And even when there were no mitigating circumstances and they knew the actions of their child or grandchild were wrong, they would still stand by them. As I was to find out.

.....

Like Dadda, Grandpa also had big, worked hands with calluses, chipped nails and sand and cement ingrained in the lines of his palms and fingers. I once saw him snap a house brick in half using nothing but his own brute force. He was proud of his strength and liked to show off, in an entertaining way, whenever the opportunity presented itself. He was a robust, fun-loving, larger-than-life character who I remembered with affection for many years. It's a shame that that memory became tainted.

2

I was a well-behaved child but I did have a stubborn streak, which was the main cause of the smacks I got from Grandma. It was a side of my nature that never came out when I was with Dadda, probably because he was always so patient and understanding.

I like to think my childish stubbornness has developed into a kind of dogged determination. I enjoy tackling tough problems; getting stuck in, attacking them head on or worrying away at them until I've solved them.

But while I could be stubborn I was never aggressive and never have been, with the one exception of the Corbin incident. Real physical violence has always disturbed me. Violence in films or books doesn't bother me but when I've seen the occasional fight in a pub or on the street it's left me feeling quite sick.

I have been the victim of physical violence myself. Twice. On both occasions the attacks were unprovoked.

.....

When I first attended St. Michael's Roman Catholic school on Astor Road I was still four years old, which would have made me one of the youngest, probably the youngest child in the school. Grandma said I was a cute little boy at the time, with soft blond curls and a smiling disposition. I had no fears about going to school as three of my older cousins and two boys I knew from Manning Road were already there. Not that this made too much difference anyway because, being of a smiling disposition, I soon made a couple of best friends: Simon Stanley and David Shepherd.

On the very first day of school I gave Simon my spade in the sand pit after another boy had snatched his away from him. He thanked me and from then on we were inseparable. David already knew Simon as they lived near each other and the three of us became a little clique, spending our break times together, walking about with our arms around each others' shoulders, playing games, or huddled in a corner of the playground.

I was quite bright at school and won a couple of prizes in my second year. One of the prizes was a big Easter egg in a box, given to me on the last day of spring term by our teacher, Mrs. Morris, for all the good work I'd done in the previous two terms. She was even more delighted with me when I suggested sharing the egg with the rest of the class. I was made to stand up while she called for three cheers and a round of applause for me. At the end of school, as we filed out of the classroom, she called me to one side, gave me a threepenny bit and told me my parents should be proud of me. When I showed it to Dadda and explained how I'd got it he rewarded me with another threepence. And when my mother heard the story she agreed that I'd been a good boy; although she said I could have brought home a bit of chocolate for her.

I think she was joking.

I loved my two years and one term at St. Michael's. They were, with just one notable exception, happy days.

.....

That notable exception was during summer term in the second year.

A new family, the Keanes, had recently arrived in the area from rural Ireland and their two sons, Pat and Danny, came to St. Michael's. Danny was in our class and Pat, a couple of years older, was in the same class as my cousin Richard. As far as I remember there were a couple of younger sisters as well. The family was pretty poor and the kids had had a tough upbringing.

"Dirty tinkers!" I heard them referred to, on more than one occasion outside church on Sundays.

Pat quickly settled down and became good friends with Richard, the black sheep of our family, but Danny was finding it hard to fit in. He was by turns either withdrawn or disruptive in the classroom, with a surly, aggressive nature that didn't endear him to Mrs. Morris or any of the other teachers. As I was something of a teacher's pet it could have been that he had a particular dislike for me.

It was playtime on the day in question. I had been inside to use the toilet and was crossing the bottom end of the juniors' playground on my way back to the infants'. Although he wasn't supposed to be in the big playground, Danny, with no friends from our class to play with, was with his brother. Most kids tended to ignore any younger siblings in school but the Keane boys were very close and Pat seemed happy to have Danny hanging around.

As I approached the corner where the two playgrounds met Danny stopped me with a hand on my shoulder. I was carrying a toy trumpet I'd won in a game at David's birthday party the previous weekend and Danny demanded I give it to him. I said "No" and tried to push past him but he pulled me around and hit me in the face. I was stunned. I froze, staring at him, not knowing what to do.

By this time Pat and Richard had seen what was going on and Richard, himself no stranger to the odd scrap, shouted:

"Don't let him do that to you, Mason. Hit him back."

But I didn't want to.

"Give it to me!" Danny demanded again.

"No. It's mine," I told him, stubborn in spite of my fear.

There was a moment's hiatus before Danny started throwing his fists at me again in a wild flurry.

"Go on Danny. Go on Danny!" yelled Pat, encouraging his little brother.

"Go on Mason, hit him back!" Richard shouted desperately, even though he could see I was taking a beating and was offering no resistance. Maybe he shared my grandparents' sense of family honour and didn't want to see me letting the side down. Or maybe he just didn't want to be associated with a coward. Whatever the case he made no attempt to help me.

When the dinner lady broke it up I was in tears, protecting myself with my arms from Danny's flailing punches. We were taken to the headmistress' office where I explained what had happened. Danny didn't argue with my version of events and I was dismissed. The dinner lady escorted me to the toilets to wash my face and then back outside to the infants' playground. On the way I saw Pat glaring at me; he knew his brother was in trouble and even though Danny had started it Pat obviously blamed me. I looked to Richard for support but all I got was contempt.

After that I kept well away from the Keane brothers in the playground. Or I made sure I was with Simon and David: safety in numbers. I doubt Danny would have picked on me when the three of us were together and I made sure he never got the chance to get hold of me on my own again.

When Grandma heard about it she threatened to go around and have it out with Danny's mother, but she never did. The Keanes had a reputation that even Grandma might have been wary of.

.....

This incident triggered another recurring nightmare. Not necessarily about Danny Keane; more about the fear and the helplessness I had experienced in the playground. In the dream I am being chased but I'm not able to run with any speed; it's like running through porridge. The harder I try the slower I get. After a while I realise that escape is impossible and I turn, swinging slow-motion punches; but, just before I feel the first blow hit me I always wake, shouting and in a cold sweat.

I still have that dream. Even though I am the strongest I have ever been in my life and I could probably knock a man out with one punch, in the dream I am as weak as a lamb.

Fortunately I don't dream very often.

.....

I never thought about taking revenge on Danny Keane; at the age of six I wasn't capable of violent thought. However as I grew older, particularly after I was attacked for the second time, I found myself fantasising acts of terrible retribution that I would carry out on various enemies and assailants, real and imagined. Despite my hatred of physical violence I couldn't help myself. In these fantasies I was either a wild man, erupting in a frenzy of violence or else a cool, calculating avenger, methodically torturing my victims.

Sometimes it worried me that I could think like that but I believed, deep down, that I could never actually behave in such a way. I could be tough and brave and violent in my head but in the real world I was the coward Richard had seen in the playground.

.....

While I lived with Dadda my nightmares rarely reached their screaming, wakening climax. He always seemed alert to the disturbances in my sleep – the moans and whimpers, the tossings and turnings – and he'd bring me around gently, wrapped in the reassuring strength of his arms, comforted by his familiar scent and soothed by his words.

"It's all right Mason, wake up. It's just a dream, just a bad dream. Wake up now. Dadda's here."

And I'd surface from that troubled dream world into the happy tranquillity of our bedroom. Then he'd carry me to his bed where he'd lie next to me, telling me stories and stroking my head until I slipped away again into peaceful sleep.

3

I have less than three years' worth of first-hand memories from my time with Dadda. That's less than a twelfth of my life. Which makes each one a dozen times more precious.

No one's memory is perfect and we all have the capacity to embellish or alter our memories, subconsciously, to create a better picture. However, I don't think I'm guilty of that when it comes to my memories of Dadda. I hope not.

These are my favourites.

.....

On the morning of Christmas Eve when I was six years old Dadda removed the big square mirror from the chimney breast in our bedroom and took it into the bathroom. He propped it up on the shelf next to his shaving mirror, stood me on the laundry box beside him and showed me how to shave. While he washed in steaming hot water he allowed me to lather up his soap brush and then apply the foam to his face, before he did the same for me. Then he gave me his spare safety razor, minus the blade, and showed me how to drag it in a pattern of smooth strokes across my skin. Down the throat from left to right, up under the jowls (using the thumb and forefinger to pull the skin tight on the neck), around the jaw-line, down the cheeks, upper lip and chin, before checking in the mirror and with the tips of the fingers to make sure the shave was clean. If there were any missed, rough patches he'd splash on a bit more hot water and back-shave against the direction of growth.

When we had finished he inspected my first ever attempt, declared it a success and gave me a few drops of aftershave lotion to dab onto my face and neck. Then we got dressed and went to the butcher's to pick up our Christmas turkey.

.....

The next day I woke early, full of anticipation. Tied to the foot of my bed was a pillowcase full of presents. I crawled down and rummaged through them in silence, feeling, shaking, rattling, sniffing, trying to work out what was in each one. I was so engrossed that when Dadda wished me a Merry Christmas I jumped and almost fell off my bed. I have no idea how long he'd been sitting up in bed watching or listening to me in the darkness.

"I haven't opened any," I told him.

The rule was that we didn't open any presents until after breakfast, which would be after I'd been to nine o'clock mass with Grandma. However Dadda didn't seem concerned with that.

"Guess what happened last night?" he whispered as he swung his legs out from under the bedclothes.

"Santa came," I replied.

"Yes. And..." He tiptoed to the window and threw back the curtains. "Look!"

The sky was still dark but there was a strange, ghostly light outside. From where I was sitting I could see what looked like the edge of a fluffy, bleached eiderdown hanging over the guttering of the bathroom roof. I slipped out of bed and padded over to the window to see the full extent of the thick layer of snow that had fallen during the night. The outlines of the houses opposite, the trees, the garden fences, Dadda's shed, everything was softened and rounded, smothered in white.

"Shall we go out?" he asked.

"Yes. Before anyone else does. Let's be the first," I replied enthusiastically.

My mother had spent the previous evening partying at a friend's house before going to midnight mass, so there was little chance of us waking her. Even so, Dadda and I dressed quickly, making as little noise as possible, before creeping downstairs. We put on our coats, scarves, hats and boots and went out into the garden.

"It looks like someone's iced everything," I said. "Like a big cake."

"Ssshh! Let's not wake anyone," he said in a low voice.

The snow was a good six inches deep. I giggled quietly in the downy, muffled silence as I jumped into deeper patches where it had drifted against walls or fences, sinking in above the tops of my wellingtons, getting snow inside them.

Dadda stood in the middle of the lawn, breathing in the lovely crisp air and breathing out plumes of mist. He watched me jumping about; looked around at the still, twinkling world of early morning; and came to a decision.

"Mason. Come here." I went over to him and he put his hands on my shoulders. "I know you're not supposed to have your presents until after mass but I've got a special surprise for you. Wait there and don't look till I tell you to."

He turned me to face the house. As I waited expectantly I heard him go into his shed and come back out again a few seconds later.

"You can turn around now," he told me.

He was holding a beautiful wooden sledge, about three feet long, painted bright red and green with shiny metal runners.

"I was going to get you a new bike but I thought we'd wait till the weather gets a bit warmer. So I made you this instead."

"Dadda! Can I have a go now? In the entry?" I asked, raising my voice.

"Ssshhh! Sshh! Shh!" he quietened me, with a finger to his lips and that shimmering smile in his eyes. I think he took as much pleasure from seeing my reaction as I did from seeing the sledge.

"It's a bit early for that, son. We don't want to wake everyone up. Here, have a sit on it."

He set it down on the snow and pushed me across the lawn while I held onto the 'reins'.

"Can I have a go in the entry before mass? When everyone's awake?" I implored him.

He looked at me sitting there; eager, excited and a little disappointed. Then he looked at his watch and came to another decision. He lifted me off the sledge, picked it up by one of its runners and took me by the hand.

"Come on," he said decisively.

We went out of the gate but instead of turning towards the top of the sloping entry he guided me down towards the street.

"Where are we going?" I asked.

"Sledging," he replied.

As we crunched our way towards the park we were the first to leave a trail on the virgin carpet of snow. The streets were deserted. Street lamps gave a pale unhealthy yellow glow to some of the houses. There were lights on in one or two windows, with shadows of movement thrown onto net curtains, but no one else had ventured out yet.

When we reached the park we climbed its biggest hill, passing through a copse of birch saplings and rhododendron: it was just like I always imagined Narnia when the children first go through the back of the wardrobe. At the top of the hill Dadda asked if I wanted to go on my own or with him. I looked down to the bottom of the steep sparkling slope where a hooped metal fence circled the pond and I worried how I would stop.

"With you," I told him.

"Come on then," he said, carefully positioning the sledge on the brink of the slope.

He tucked me in front of him and rocked us forwards and backwards a couple of times to bed the runners for a good start.

"Are you ready?" he asked.

"We mustn't make any noise, must we Dadda?"

On the edge of the park there was a row of semi-detached houses that must have been in earshot. Dadda glanced over at them.

"Make as much noise as you want, son. It's Christmas. Here we go!" And he pushed off.

We hurtled down the hillside, gathering momentum, skimming over the ground at fantastic speed, whooping and yahooing until Dadda dug in his heels towards the bottom, bringing us to a halt ten or twelve feet short of the railings. I burst out laughing, like a lunatic; partly from the thrill of the ride, partly with relief that we hadn't crashed.

"Was that good?" Dadda asked.

I was laughing so hard, gulping in lungfuls of freezing air, that I started coughing and choking. Eventually I managed to control myself enough to splutter and answer:

"Let's do it again Dadda."

"Come on then," he said, picking up the sledge.

But before we made the climb back to the top Dadda took my hand and we paused. In the silence of that Christmas Day morning, with the panting breath of our exhilaration rising like clouds of steam above us, we stood hand in hand and surveyed the silvery expanse of that snow-covered hillside; pure and perfect except for the parallel tracks of our sledge. The mark of our passing. Dadda's and mine.

If I could freeze or distil a single moment from my life and exist in that moment alone, that would be it.

After several more rides we went home, arriving in time for cereal with hot milk before I went off to church with Grandma. When we got back my mother was up and, after more breakfast, I was allowed to open the rest of my presents. I got some lovely gifts but the best thing about that day was the trip to the park with Dadda and my new sledge. It was made even more special because no one else ever knew about it; our secret adventure into a private, magical world where we and we alone existed.

.....

Among the presents I got that Christmas was a toy tool kit, given to me as a result of the interest I had started showing in Dadda's work. I had often watched him when he was whittling in the garden but I had never really taken much notice of what he did inside his shed. But during the previous autumn I started asking questions about what he was doing and what the various tools were used for. I was fascinated by them: saws, hammers, drills, screwdrivers, planes and so on. Dadda kept them hanging from nails and brackets in their allotted places high on the shed walls, well out of the reach of an inquisitive child. He promised to show me how to use them when I was older but said they were too dangerous for a little boy to play with. This, of course, made me even more keen to get my hands on them; so when I got my own tool kit that Christmas I was delighted. Over the next year I spent many happy hours sawing, drilling, screwing and hammering, making imaginary items. And from time to time, under close supervision, Dadda let me handle some of his tools, although I was never allowed to take them to a piece of wood.

.....

After my mother took me away I didn't touch any tools again until I was at secondary school. Danny, my mother's boyfriend who we moved in with, wasn't much of a handyman.

"I pay other people to do that sort of thing," he explained arrogantly.

.....

Twice a year Dadda visited the grave where the two Lauras were buried together. He went on his ex-wife's birthday and on the anniversary of their deaths, which would have been baby Laura's birthday. I went with him once, when I was six.

We set off early on a warm sunny day to drive the three miles or so to the cemetery, a large corporation concern which also had a crematorium near the main gate. Dadda had picked some pansies from our garden and made them into a small posy that I held solemnly on the journey. As we walked through the graves I asked him why Laura had been buried rather than cremated. He said that was what her parents had wanted so he had agreed to their wishes. He didn't know if Laura had a preference herself; they'd never thought to talk about it.

The grave has a plain white headstone and white stone chippings covering it. It was well tended that day we visited and there was a blue vase containing some wilting flowers that Dadda removed as soon as we arrived. He pointed out a standpipe next to a rubbish bin on one of the paths and asked me to dump the dead flowers and fill the vase with fresh water. When I returned he was pulling up some blades of grass and weeds that were poking through the chippings, which he then raked over with his hand to give them an even spread. He cleared a small patch just in front of the headstone and replaced the vase, packing the chippings around to secure it before putting in the pansies. He knelt back on one knee and drew me to him, sitting me on the thigh of his other leg. I watched him as he stared pensively at the grave. He didn't look pained like he did that time Big Mick took him from Grandpa's party.

"Are you sad, Dadda?" I asked.

"A little bit," he answered.

"Is it sad when someone dies?"

"When it's someone you love, it is. To have that person taken away from you and know you'll never see them again."

Under the bright sun the pansies shone vibrant yellow and crimson against the white stones of the grave.

"I like to remember all the nice things about Laura," he told me. "To think of her alive and laughing. That's the worst thing about baby Laura; I never got to know her so I can't picture her."

"She's like big Laura, only smaller," I suggested.

Dadda laughed dryly. I rested my hands on his, which were folded across my tummy. We sat in silence for a while until I noticed a couple of blades of grass Dadda had missed on the grave and got up to pull them out. He watched me fondly for a few moments before speaking again.

"The thing is, son, it does no good living in the past. And, by the same token, it's no good living for the future because we never know what's around the corner. If you want my advice you should try to live for the present; one day at a time."

He paused for a moment before continuing.

"I'll never forget Laura and baby Laura till the day I die but I can't spend the rest of my life being miserable. And Laura wouldn't have wanted that either."

He held out his hand to me. I crossed to him and was gathered up in a strong, tender hug. Then he held me at arm's length and looked me squarely in the eyes.

"And, anyway, I've got you now," he said, his face breaking out into a big smile as he hugged me again.

.....

On my seventh birthday, true to his word, Dadda gave me a new bicycle. It was actually a second-hand one that he had done up, but that didn't matter to me. He'd kept it at Big Mick's house where he worked on it in secret, giving it a fresh coat of paint, a new saddle and a mechanical overhaul. I already had a bike that used to have trainer wheels on but it was getting too small for me by the time I was seven. The new one, with a deep blue frame and a red leather saddle, was quite a lot bigger; it was a stretch for me to reach the ground with my tiptoe when I sat on it.

"That should last you a couple of years," said Dadda when he gave it to me. "We'll get you one with gears next time."

He'd taught me to ride the old one at the top end of Farm Road where a grass verge separated the gently sloping pavement from the road. I'd mastered it with the trainer wheels in no time at all and Dadda was as keen as I was to take them off so I could learn to ride it properly.

"I used to ride everywhere when I was a young man," he told me as he unbolted the stabilisers. "Before I got a car. It's a great way to see the world, Mason. Travelling at a civilised speed with time to look around you. Getting plenty of exercise and fresh air. Maybe I'll get another bike when you're a bit older. We could go on cycling trips together."

A couple of minutes later he was running alongside the bike, steadying me with a hand on the back of the saddle as I pedalled furiously and confidently up Farm Road.

.....

I loved my blue bike for the three months I had it. Seven years later I was saddened to see it again, rusted and covered in cobwebs under a pile of junk in what was then the Morgans' shed.

.....

In later years I thought about making one of my European trips by bicycle but I couldn't be bothered getting all the gear: bike, panniers, riding cape and so on. It would have cost too much. Anyway,

I preferred hitchhiking as it meant I didn't have to make any decisions about where I went.

I had a couple more bikes when I was growing up but I only used them for riding to school. I never really regarded them as playthings and I never made any trips of the kind Dadda talked about.

These days I have a battered old black delivery bike which I get out sometimes on a Sunday and ride into the local countryside; pootling along at a leisurely pace, taking in the scenery as I search for a decent pub to have a quiet drink in. (I don't ride it to work because that would be out of character.) On those warm lazy Sundays I like to imagine Dadda as a young man, possibly with Laura beside him, roaming the country lanes on his bicycle, delighting in the nature of rural Britain.

.....

Other than the specific incidents I have mentioned my overall impression of the time I spent with Dadda is one of happiness and fulfilment. Our day-to-day lives were not extraordinary but they were pleasant and contented, punctuated by moments of real joy derived from the simplest little things. That was the way things were and I don't believe I have allowed nostalgia to shape my perception of that time. I was a certain person back then. When I was taken away from Dadda that person was left behind and I became someone else. I became nobody.

4

For the first seven years of my life I had little to do with my mother. She treated me like an uninterested sister might treat a younger brother, doing the absolute minimum when it came to helping with my upbringing. For the most part she got on with her own life; the fact that she shared a house with Dadda and me was incidental.

"Go and ask your Dadda."

I don't know how many times I must have heard her say that.

She wasn't unkind to me – she even played with me sometimes, in a detached kind of way, when she was in the mood – but she was never tactile. Two of my older cousins, Donna and Carmel, loved to baby me, smothering me with kisses and cuddles, treating me like a living doll. My mother just didn't have that maternal instinct. Having wished me dead throughout her pregnancy it's hardly any surprise that she was indifferent towards me after I was born. She had more important things to be getting on with.

For those seven years we hardly knew each other. But she was still my mother.

.....

If I have inherited anything from my mother it's her independence. She was a free spirit as a teenager and she stayed that way throughout the time I knew her. I used to think she needed the various boyfriends and lovers she had after we left Dadda, but she didn't. She used every one of them. Manipulated them. Even when we lived with them she managed to have a life of her own. Most of the fights she had with her boyfriends started because they tried to restrict her freedom or complained about it. She always won.

When we moved away from Dadda and my mother's relatives, she had Danny. Then, when we left Danny there was Roger. And after him there was Andy. And, towards the end, there was a string of one-offs and no-hopers. But in the gaps between boyfriends she always had me there. So when I left her, by which time she was almost totally cut off from her family, she was on her own for the first time; apart from the awful Brenda.

I wonder if she's still on her own. And, if she is, whether she has learned the difference between independence and loneliness?

5

During my final term at St. Michael's I continued to be a lively, participatory class member and a bright student, with an interest and aptitude in all subjects. I got on well with our new class teacher, Miss

Robson. I had lots of friends; although Simon and David were still my best friends. And there had been no more trouble with Danny Keane.

At the start of term Grandma had decided I didn't need picking up from school any more, so she no longer came to meet me at the gate. Instead I was helped across Astor Road by the elderly, white-coated lollipop man – who I thought looked like Mr. Chips from the film *Goodbye Mr. Chips* – and I made the rest of the journey on my own. I used to enjoy that solitary walk back to Grandma's house, where I would stay until Dadda or my mother collected me. I used to dawdle along in a world of my own, investigating little holes in the crumbling cement of the front garden walls, probing for some unexpected treasure. I'm not sure what I hoped to find exactly but it was never anything more interesting than an old ice-lolly stick, a screwed-up sweet wrapper or, if I was lucky, an insect nest.

When I wasn't poking my fingers into holes in garden walls I'd scour the gutter, or search behind gateposts or around the bases of the trees that lined the street. Sometimes I'd be lucky and find a penny or halfpenny that I'd spend on sweets in old Mrs. Taylor's shop on the corner of Manning Road and Astor Road. Then I'd go back to Grandma's house and sit on the front steps, chewing or sucking the sweets with slow relish while I watched the junior school children, who got out of school fifteen minutes later than us, passing by with their mothers. I used to feel very mature knowing I was allowed to make the journey on my own.

.....

There was a real Indian summer that year that lasted well into late October, maybe even November. I remember there were many evenings when it was warm enough for me to play out in the garden after tea while Dadda worked in his shed or sat on its step, smoking his pipe. Life seemed to be going along pretty much as before. If there was any noticeable change in my mother or a hint of what was to come I wasn't aware of it. Nor was Dadda.

The second time I saw Dadda looking distressed we were visiting his mother in hospital just after she'd had a stroke. I don't think he wanted to take me with him but there was no one else around to look after me so he had no choice.

I didn't see Nanna very often. Before her stroke I saw her maybe two or three times a year. I think she had a bit of a problem accepting me because I wasn't Dadda's natural child. That's the impression I was given by Grandma years later. I know Dadda used to visit her more often on his own.

Even before we got to the ward, as we walked through the high, wide, polished corridors, Dadda looked uncomfortable. Nanna was in a ward with seven other elderly ladies in various stages of mental and physical decrepitude. I remember thinking how frail and withered they all looked, even though a couple of them were sitting up talking to visitors.

Nanna was either unconscious or in a very deep sleep when we got to her bed. Dadda examined her gently, pushing some strands of hair off her face and feeling her brow before sitting in the rickety wooden chair next to the iron bedstead. He took her hand and spoke to her, watching her face, searching for some reaction or sign of recognition. After a while he fell silent and looked around the ward at the other patients. The old lady in the next bed was dribbling in her sleep. Another called for a bedpan and a nurse closed the curtains around her bed. A third shuffled down the ward, passing the end of Nanna's bed, muttering to herself as she went. Dadda watched her progress with that same pained look on his face that I'd seen on the day of Grandpa's party. When he spoke he addressed me but I think he was just thinking aloud.

"It's not fair, Mason. Most of us don't ask too much from life; just to get through it with some semblance of dignity. But even that gets taken away from some of us. Nature can be so cruel."

Nanna didn't wake while we were there. Eventually Dadda had a brief chat to one of the nurses and we left. On the way home we did something we'd never done before and never did again; we stopped at a pub. I had a bottle of pop and some crisps with a blue bag of salt in them; Dadda had a pint of mild and a glass of whisky, which he drank down in one. Then he sat in silence for quite some time, nursing his beer and staring into space.

On the day of Grandpa's party I wasn't fully aware of Dadda's pain, I just remember the strange look on his face. There in the pub his distress was plain to see. I didn't understand why he was so upset but I knew I needed to cheer him up. Instinctively, perhaps, I did the right thing; I got him to talk about something he loved. I asked him what kind of wood the table and the bar were made of. Initially his answers were superficial, almost to the point of being curt, but I managed to coax more out of him by asking about the mirrors and wooden mouldings behind the bar. Gradually he warmed to the task, describing the processes that had been used, identifying the types of wood and explaining why that particular type of wood had been chosen. By the time we left the pub and headed for home he was a bit more like his usual self.

Nanna was taken to an old people's home a few weeks later and lived on for another three years, although I didn't find out she'd died until I was fourteen.

.....

Towards the end of that last term at St. Mike's I started looking forward to the Christmas holidays. The weather was getting colder with snow expected, so I was hoping I'd be able to take out my sledge again. There would be Christmas Day with all that entails and the holidays meant more time to spend with Dadda.

The last day of term was full of festive cheer. During the traditional class party after lunch Miss Robson handed out three special prizes, stocking-shaped selection boxes, one of which was awarded to me. We played games; she read the last instalment of a story she'd been telling us throughout the term; and there was jelly, ice cream and fizzy pop all round.

We were let out of school early and I said goodbye to Simon and David at the school gate, wishing them a happy Christmas.

"See you next year," we shouted to each other.

On the curb of Astor Road the lollipop man asked about my

selection box, congratulating me when I told him it was a prize.

It was a cold day so I didn't hang about getting back to Grandma's. In those days the streets weren't lined with parked cars the way they are now and, as I approached Grandma's house, I noticed a blue car outside Dadda's. There was a man sitting in the driver's seat; for some reason I stopped and watched him for a few moments. He looked restless, checking his watch, drumming his fingers on the steering wheel and peering around him out of the car windows.

I went up the entry and into Grandma's yard. There was a football there, left by one of my cousins, and I kicked it up the steps onto the lawn. As I turned to open the back door I heard raised voices and was surprised when I realised one of them was my mother's. What was she doing home? Why wasn't she at work? I assumed she must have been let out early as well, because of Christmas.

The door was ajar between the kitchen and living room where Grandma and my mother were talking heatedly, their voices rising to shouts. Disconcerted, I stopped in the kitchen and listened.

"After all he's done you've at least got to let him see the child! To say goodbye!" Grandma was saying.

"Why? It'll be easier on everyone if we just go."

"Easier on you, you mean."

"Look, I don't want to upset anyone more than I have to."

"Don't want to upset anyone?! You'll destroy the poor man. He idolises that child."

When I pushed the door open they stopped shouting and stared at me. I didn't know what was happening but something was obviously wrong.

"What are you doing home?!" demanded Grandma, looking at the clock on the mantelpiece.

I was taken aback by the severity of her tone, which was probably an overspill from her conversation with my mother.

"We were let out early," I answered with a trembling lower lip. In an attempt to mollify her I held up the selection box. "I got a prize off Miss Robson."

Grandma calmed down enough to congratulate me.

"Oh! Well done. Good boy. Here," she said, grabbing up her purse from an armchair and giving me a sixpence. "Go to Mrs. Taylor's and get yourself some sweets. Then go home. Your mother will be there in a minute."

For once I didn't want any sweets. Having spent the afternoon eating jelly and ice cream and a couple of items out of the selection box, I'd had enough. I was also aware that Grandma never gave me money for sweets. Ever. Not even as a reward for winning prizes. Something was definitely wrong but I knew better than to question her. I left my selection box on Grandma's sofa and went out. As I crossed the yard I could see her watching from behind the net curtains to make sure I went out of the back gate.

When I came back from Mrs. Taylor's, with an unopened packet of chews, the man was still in his car. He seemed to take notice of me as I turned into the entry next to Dadda's house. I went in the back door and straight to the front room where I watched him out of the bay window while I waited for my mother to come home. I didn't like the look of him. After some time my mother appeared with Grandma who sailed past the car, making an obvious display of ignoring its occupant. My mother stopped next to the car, opened the passenger door and said something to the man before she followed Grandma up the entry. The man looked at his watch again and started up the engine. As the car pulled away Grandma came into the room behind me.

"Did you get your sweets?" she asked.

I showed her the chews and she asked if there was any change, which I gave her. She stood looking at me pityingly.

"You poor child," she muttered. "God knows you've done nothing to deserve this."

I still had no idea what was going on but I was overwhelmed suddenly by a sense of foreboding and I burst into tears. Grandma picked me up and hugged me and hushed me and told me it was going to be all right. Which was a lie. I wanted to ask who the man in the car was but didn't dare; somehow I knew he was involved in whatever was going on.

The next couple of hours, while we waited for Dadda to come home, were almost unbearable. There was a sharp, prickly tension between Grandma and my mother, who couldn't sit still for more than two minutes, pacing between the living room and the front room, watching the clock. I felt suffocated and was relieved when Grandpa showed up.

"What's this all about?" he asked, waving a note scribbled on a scrap of paper.

I tried to go to him but Grandma pushed him back into the kitchen, closing the door behind them. I heard her talking to him urgently in whispered tones and then Grandpa exploding:

"Oh, God no! For the love of Jesus not now?!"

I had no idea what she'd said to him but his reaction set me off crying again. My mother, who was in the living room with me, made no effort to comfort me. I'm not sure she even noticed I was crying. She sat on the arm of the settee, chewing her lip nervously and watching the kitchen door. After a few minutes Grandma came back into the room followed by Grandpa who picked me up and tried to console me.

"Does this child know what's going on?" he asked.

My mother stared at her feet and Grandma shook her head.

"Holy mother of God," he muttered.

His eyes were burning into my mother's head and shoulders.

"Why now?" he asked her. "With Christmas coming up?"

"What difference does that make?" my mother snapped back.

"Don't you raise your voice to me," he snarled threateningly.

"It's for his good," she continued, trying to sound reasonable. "I waited until term was over so as not to disturb him at school. God knows I've waited long enough."

He glared at her before taking me into the front room where he sat me on his lap and stroked my head, holding me close to him.

"You're a good boy, Mason," he kept telling me. "You're a good boy," as we sat in the bay, looking out for Dadda to come home.

In a moment of pure farce Dadda's car pulled up outside the house at exactly the same moment as the man returned in his blue car. They parked one behind the other. As Dadda got out of his car, picking up his tool bag from the passenger seat, he hardly even glanced at the man. Why should he? He wasn't to know the man was about to change our lives. I saw him but I was so relieved to see Dadda that that's all I cared about. Everything would be all right now.

I ran through the house and met Dadda as he came through the back gate, hurling myself at him desperately. He swung me up and hugged and kissed me. I wanted everything to be normal and tried to put the previous hours out of my mind. Tried to pretend they hadn't happened. I burbled on about my selection box and the party and the games we'd played while he stood in the yard, holding me in the crook of an arm, smiling and nodding. I wanted to stop him from going into the house where Grandma, Grandpa and my mother were waiting. I knew intuitively that once he went inside something bad was going to happen.

"Come on," he interrupted me, eventually. "Let's get the dinner on. Not that you'll be hungry after all you've eaten today."

He carried me into the kitchen where Grandma and Grandpa were waiting. By the looks on their faces he knew that something was wrong. His immediate reaction was to ask if anything had happened to my mother. Grandpa said that she was fine but there was something else.

"Stephen, I need to talk to you," he said, taking me from Dadda and passing me to Grandma who took me through to the front room. My mother wasn't in the living room as we passed through. She'd made herself scarce, hiding upstairs.

Grandma and I sat in the bay, where I noticed that the man in the blue car kept looking at our house and checking his watch again. I pointed this out to Grandma, who nodded absently; her attention was focused on the door to the living room.

I have no idea how long it took Grandpa to explain the situation to Dadda. Nor how he went about it. Nor how Dadda responded. Grandma and I sat there for what seemed like an age before Grandpa came in and ushered Grandma into the living room. I asked Grandpa if I could go and see Dadda and he said "In a minute." He told me again that I was a good boy and that I had to be brave for Dadda. Once again that feeling of apprehension came over me, worse than ever and tears started to well up in my eyes.

"Now, now," said Grandpa, picking me up and hugging me.

As I held him around his neck I saw through my tears, through the net curtain of the bay window in which I'd never again sit waiting for my Dadda to come home, my mother putting a bag into the boot of the blue car. The man stood next to her looking anxious. She said something that seemed to calm him and he got back into the driver's seat and started the engine. She came around to the passenger side and climbed into the back seat.

As I watched the door opened behind me and I heard Dadda calling to me softly. I turned and for the third time in my life saw that look on his face; only this time the pain was more clearly, more excruciatingly obvious than ever before.

"Son," he said, holding out his arms to me.

I jumped off Grandpa's lap and threw myself at Dadda again. Grandma was standing behind him with tears in her eyes, which scared me almost as much as the look on Dadda's face.

"Mason," he said, "I've tried to understand this but I can't. I don't understand it so I can't explain it to you. Maybe your mother can."

He held me as tightly as one of the vices in his shed.

"Your mother is going away and she's taking you with her. She's your mother and that's her right. I can't stop her. But this is not what I want, son. Never forget that. No matter what anyone tells you, this is not what I want. Just remember that I love you as much as I've ever loved anything; even my Laura. I love you just as much as I love her."

At the time those words had no meaning to me. I hardly even heard them. 'Your mother is going away and she's taking you with her' were the only words that registered. Beyond that all I knew was that I was more frightened than I'd ever been in my life. I clung on to Dadda with all my might as the tears cascaded down my cheeks.

Dadda didn't cry, not while I was still there, but there was anguish carved into his face as he looked at me for the last time.

"Mason, I'll write to you and, if I can, I'll come and see you. And whatever happens I'll never forget you. Be a good boy, Mason. I love you, son." And he tried desperately to smile before he kissed me and handed me to Grandpa, who carried me out and passed me to my mother in the back of the blue car.

I cried out for Dadda but before I knew what was happening the door had been slammed and I was being driven away. My mother hung on to me so firmly, trying to stop me kicking and screaming, that I didn't even get the chance to look out of the back window to see Dadda's house, Dadda, my happiness and the spirit of a small boy, all disappearing behind me.

6

Dadda never did visit me. And if he wrote letters they were never posted. But that was through no fault of his.

My grandparents may not have agreed with my mother's decision to leave and take me with her, they might even have argued against it but in the end they didn't stand in her way. And they hadn't finished yet.

Years later, in one of her vindictive rants, my mother informed me that her parents, faithful to her instructions, had refused to give Dadda the details of our whereabouts. They allowed their precious ideal of solidarity and family honour to destroy, for a second time, the life of a man whom I had often heard my grandmother refer to as a saint. He was a friend who, having lost his own family, made a sacrifice for the reputation of theirs. And that's how they repaid him.

.....

I cried myself to sleep in the back of the blue car. When I woke up a few hours later, exhausted and confused, my mother introduced me to her boyfriend, Danny. I had many reasons to dislike him, his name being one of them as it reminded me of Danny Keane. My mother told me we were going to have an exciting new life in an exciting new place. Whenever I asked about Dadda she changed the subject.

For some reason I remembered my selection box and asked where it was, to be told it had been left behind at Grandma's. Irrationally this triggered another bout of hysteria. As he drove, Danny spoke to me over his shoulder, promising me as much chocolate as I could eat when we got 'home', as he called it. Or, indeed, anything else I wanted. I was to learn that this was his answer to most problems.

Devastated by everything that was happening I cried myself to sleep again.

In the early hours of the following morning, having driven through the night, we arrived at Danny's flat where we were to live for the next five years.

.....

It's the greatest mystery of my life.

Dadda said he didn't understand it. He said maybe my mother would explain it but I never asked her and she never volunteered the information.

From the moment she knew she was pregnant she hadn't wanted me. She wished me dead inside her. For the first seven years of my life she practically ignored me. So why, when she made the decision to leave, did she take me with her?

Why?

PART THREE

1

I woke up in a strange bed in a strange room. I must have been fast asleep when we arrived because I had no memory of being put there. It took a while before I came to my senses and had a good look around. There was a thick red fitted carpet on the floor (I had never seen a fitted one before); the walls were decorated with a green and red vertical stripe wallpaper; a flimsy looking chest of drawers stood in one corner of the room; and the curtains, through which the winter sun shone weakly, were made of a coarse emerald-green material. It was nothing like the magnolia-painted wood-chipped bedrooms in Dadda's house and I didn't like it.

Once I was more awake I decided to go in search of someone – or something – familiar. Bleary and drained from the previous night's trauma I went into the hallway, rubbing my puffy red eyes. The first thing I noticed was that there didn't seem to be any stairs; as I'd never been in a flat before I found this very confusing. I padded through to the lounge, which was liberally sprinkled with gaudy kitsch decorations and ornaments: lava lamp; spherical orange portable television set; psychedelic pictures on the walls; garish furniture covers; ovoid bamboo chair hanging from the ceiling. This was a world apart from the sturdy sensible furnishings of Dadda's or my grandparents' houses. Under other circumstances I might have been fascinated, enchanted even, by all these bright unusual things. As it was I found them alien and unsettling. The kitchen (a pastel blue formica hell) was like a tip; unwashed crockery and cutlery lay scattered about the surfaces and the bin was overflowing with food packets, empty tins and vegetable peelings. The bathroom smelled of damp towels and when I pushed open the door of the other bedroom, where my mother and Danny were welded together in a comatose lump under the blankets, that stank too, of cigarette smoke, alcohol, stale sweat and aftershave.

"Where's Dadda?" I asked, but my question fell on deaf ears.

I didn't want to go into the bedroom and it was obvious they weren't going to wake up so I wandered back to the lounge trying to hold back the tide that was rising up inside me. I felt like I did that day in the park when I watched Dadda's car driving away; terrified and abandoned. Regarding the bizarre knick-knacks suspiciously I crossed to the hanging chair, which I swung a couple of times before climbing into it, like a child climbing back into the womb. As I lay there, curled up like a foetus, trying to stifle the sobs in my throat and blinking back the tears in my eyes, I gave in to a wave of tiredness and was rocked gently back to sleep.

I woke to find Danny sitting on the sofa, as he called it. (We would have called it a settee. And the lounge would have been the living room.) He was smoking a cigarette and drinking tea. When he noticed I was awake he welcomed me to his home with these words: "That's my chair. I don't mind you sitting in it when I'm not here, but when I am it's mine. And it's not a swing or a toy, so go easy with it."

.....

In fairness to Danny, although I never really liked him, he showed more interest in me than my mother did during the five years we spent with him. Having given up his bachelor status he seemed keen to play the family man. Initially at least. He was always coming up with ideas of things we could do together but he was frustrated by a lack of interest and enthusiasm: from me because I resented him for the part he had played in taking me away from Dadda; and from my mother because she had no interest in anything but herself.

2

Danny's flat was above his hairdressing salon, a thriving enterprise situated in a row of shops on a busy road in a predominantly residential area. When we arrived the idea was for my mother to work in the salon - shampooing, sweeping up, that kind of thing – while he taught her the skills of the trade. And for the first year and a half that's what happened, until she tired of spending twenty-four hours a day in Danny's company. Most of his customers were middle-aged women who went to the salon to listen to his risqué banter as much as for his abilities as a hairdresser. After eighteen months of working alongside him my mother announced she was "sick and tired of listening to him joking and flirting with those silly old bags". She got a job in a department store in the town centre, reclaimed her autonomy and started developing her own social life independent of him. He didn't like this but he didn't have much choice. At first he complained but she merely ignored him, telling him to stop being such a big baby. Then, as time went on, the complaints turned into hints at infidelity and, finally, out and out accusations. (Accusations that I later discovered were well founded.) She would tell him to stop being so paranoid and they would end up arguing; but my mother had a smart mouth with an answer for everything and always got the better of him. On a couple of occasions when Danny threatened to throw her out she played her trump card, claiming he'd dragged us away from our life in Manning Road. That we were his responsibility and he'd better make sure he fulfilled that responsibility. I don't know what her "or else" would have been if he'd challenged her, but he never did.

However, the first eighteen months was a relatively happy and harmonious time in their lives, if not in mine.

.....

During the early hours of my second night in Danny's flat I woke screaming and crying from a bad dream. With no Dadda there to comfort me I was frightened to find myself alone in the dark. When my calls went unanswered I got out of bed and bumped my way into the hallway. Still uncertain of the geography of the flat I felt my way to the end of the corridor where I practically fell into the kitchen, knocking an empty milk bottle to the floor. The crash woke Danny who came rushing out of his bedroom, pulling on some pyjama bottoms, wielding a shoe and shouting threats at the burglars he must have thought he was disturbing. He turned the light on but didn't see the glass until it was too late, lodging several large chunks in the sole of his bare foot. He shouted out in pain and anger, which set me off crying again and our combined yelling and bawling woke my mother. She stumbled as far as the bedroom doorway, where she stood squinting at us sleepily for a few seconds before mumbling something unintelligible, ruffling her hair and going straight back to bed. This left Danny, who was bleeding heavily onto the beige-and-brown patterned lino, to deal with me, his injuries and the mess on the floor. His problems were compounded when he took me back to my room and found I'd wet the bed. Unable to cope with all this and the beginnings of the hangover he was going to have in the morning he told me I'd just have to try to avoid the damp patch. He took off my sodden pyjama bottoms, moved my pillows to the foot of the bed and picked me up. It was the first time I'd been that close to him and he stank of cigarettes and alcohol, as he did most evenings. He dumped me into the bed and pulled the blankets over me before hopping to the door, which I asked him to leave open with the hall light on.

.....

Dadda always smelled of pipe tobacco and sometimes of beer or whisky but these smells on him were never offensive. As a matter of fact I liked them. However the same smells on Danny repulsed me. Was that something to do with chemicals? The combination of those smells with the individual's pheromones? Or was it because I disliked Danny? Or maybe because, where he was concerned, I never associated those smells with comfort?

I don't know.

.....

After that night I always had to have some light in my bedroom and the door left ajar. The dark had never really bothered me before; Dadda had always assured me there was nothing to be afraid of and with him close by I believed that. But without him the dark represented fear and uncertainty. And loneliness.

Eventually I would learn to feel at home in the dark and dead of night; and accept and embrace solitude. But that would be many years later.

.....

My fourth day in Danny's flat was Christmas Day.

He had gone out on Christmas Eve and bought a tree that was decorated with a few strands of red and green tinsel and a single set of fairy lights. It was then placed as much out of the way as possible, in an alcove behind his beloved hanging chair. He made it quite clear that, under normal circumstances, he wouldn't have bothered and he seemed to expect some display of gratitude. As it was I couldn't have cared less and I'm fairly sure my mother couldn't either.

When I woke on Christmas morning there was no sack of presents at the foot of my bed. Not even a stocking. I crossed to the window, pulled back the curtains and looked out at the untidy blue-brick yard at the back of the salon. In the pre-dawn light I could see drizzling sleety rain. It was shaping up to be a cold, grey day. What a contrast to the previous year.

In the lounge I turned on the fairy lights, which illuminated a small pile of presents strewn carelessly around the foot of the Christmas tree. I read the labels and identified a couple for me, recognising Grandma's spidery writing on one of them and Dadda's strong, careful hand on another. This re-opened the floodgates. I took the package and climbed once again into Danny's suspended chair, where I cried myself back to sleep, soaking the paper of Dadda's present which I held pressed to my cheek.

My mother woke me in a panic with a barked instruction to get ready for church. While we raced around, pulling on our Sunday best, Danny sludged about in a vile lime green candlewick dressing gown, looking for his cigarettes. He stayed in the dressing gown when he drove us to the nearest Catholic church, where he waited outside in the car until mass was over. When we got back to the flat my mother turned on the television and told me I could open my presents. Then she followed Danny back to their bedroom, closing and locking the door behind them.

My mother had given me a compendium of games - ludo, snakes

and ladders, lotto, 'Happy Families' - which was fine apart from the fact that I had no one to play with. Grandma and Grandpa gave me a bright yellow cardigan (hand-knitted by Grandma), a gun that shot suckered darts and a handkerchief with the letter 'M' embroidered in one corner. There was a small box of chocolates from one of my mother's sisters, which I ate in lieu of breakfast. And Dadda's present, which I saved until last.

Holding the neatly wrapped package in one hand I ran my fingers over the lines of his handwriting, trying to feel him and his love in the way he felt things in lumps of wood. Taking great pains not to rip the paper I peeled back the wrapping to reveal a box, inside which I found an instamatic camera. I took it out carefully and inspected it. Although I had no idea how to use it I cherished it dearly that Christmas morning. I'm sure Dadda would have got me a film for it and had probably even bought and wrapped one before I was taken away. As it was, the presents I received that Christmas Day had been gathered hastily by Grandma and thrust into one of my mother's bags as she was sneaking out of Dadda's back door. So I suppose I was lucky to get anything.

After some time handling the camera, holding the viewfinder up to my eye and clicking at nothing in particular, I re-wrapped it. I took it to my bedroom and placed it in one of the drawers of the dressing table. I didn't use it for another four years or so but I often took it out and gave it a clean with a soft cloth, making sure it never got dirty or clogged up with dust.

I spent the rest of that Christmas Day morning watching television, looking out of the windows or playing board games on my own. When my mother and Danny eventually surfaced they washed and dressed quickly, Danny grabbed a big pile of presents from the bottom of his wardrobe and we drove to his sister's house for Christmas dinner.

After we'd eaten the adults spent the afternoon and evening in the front room, drinking, smoking and getting to know my mother. I was left in the living room with Danny's nephew and nieces who tried to involve me in their games. I refused sullenly, preferring to watch from the sanctuary of a battered old armchair as they played with their new toys. When their father, Colin, came through on his way to the outside toilet he tried to cheer me up and get me to join in with the others but I just withdrew further. After a couple of minutes he gave up and went outside. On his way back he threw some coal from a scuttle onto the fire, which belched dusty, acrid fumes into the room to join the cigarette smoke that was drifting in from the front room. My eyes smarted, becoming sore and heavy, my head started to ache and the next thing I knew I woke up in half-darkness in my hideously striped bedroom. I had wet the bed again and Christmas Day was over.

.....

Four years later Boxing Day lived up to its name when Danny and Colin came to blows. Danny had walked in on Colin giving my mother what they claimed was a harmless Christmas kiss in the kitchen. It may well have been harmless, I don't know, but by this time Danny was eaten up with suspicions and jealousy. And he had every reason to suspect her. There were accusations and threats. Voices were raised. Fingers were thrust in faces. There was some pushing and shoving and then Colin snapped and swung a big arcing haymaker that brushed the tip of Danny's nose. Colin's wife, Eileen, tried to calm things down. Colin apologised and tried to make the peace with the offer of another drink. One of their kids started bawling. My mother, as was her wont, remained calmly on the periphery, rising above the whole mess that she had been partly responsible for creating. Meanwhile Danny was absolutely furious. He shouted a final threat at Colin, grabbed my mother by the wrist, called her some name or other and dragged her out. I followed behind but stopped at the door to wish Colin, Eileen and their family a Merry Christmas. I wish I could say I'd done it ironically but that wouldn't be true.

It had been an ugly scene but I wasn't too unhappy about it, apart from having to listen to the inevitable row in the car. It meant we got home earlier and I could go to my room and get on with the book I was reading.

3

In January I started attending the Sacred Heart School. My bed-wetting had continued through the Christmas holiday period and on my first day of school, already feeling timid and unconfident, I wet myself in class. This led to teasing and name-calling as a result of which I spent playtimes on my own, hidden away in some quiet corner of the playground.

This incontinence carried on for quite some time and I remember Danny discussing it with my mother, expressing what seemed like genuine concern. She reckoned I was probably still adjusting to the move. She told him that I would be all right in time and he let it drop. After all, she was my mother so she must have known best.

As time went by I became more and more withdrawn at Sacred Heart. The quality of my schoolwork suffered, with reading being the only subject in which I showed any kind of interest or development. As the teachers had no idea I had been a prize-winning student at St. Mike's there was no reason they should have been surprised or concerned. They probably just thought I was a bit slow.

I enjoyed going to St. Mike's and looked forward to turning up each day. During the first two terms at Sacred Heart I spent every day longing for the final bell to ring. Wishing away the time so I could get back to a home that held no comfort or love but where I would, at least, be left alone. Where I would watch television until my mother or Danny arrived home and turned to the programmes they wanted to watch. Then I'd shut myself away in my cheerless green-and-red room and escape to other worlds between the pages of a book or in my own imagination.

.....

In the summer holidays my isolation was even more pronounced as I never got to know any other kids in the area, so I had no one to play with. The paved area in front of the shops was neither safe nor particularly stimulating so either I stayed indoors, or mucked about among the empty cardboard boxes and debris in the shabby back yard, or spent time in the local library. I was quite happy there, spending hours at a time in the children's reading corner, sitting next to a window beneath a painted frieze of Snow White And The Seven Dwarfs. I'd read or simply watch other young children brought in by their mothers or elder brothers and sisters. At those times I felt the sense of maturity and independence I used to feel while sitting on Grandma's steps after I'd walked home on my own from St. Mike's. Sometimes one of the librarians might tell me, in a kindly way, that I should be outside running around in the sunshine but there was neither much room, nor much sunshine, in the high-walled yard behind Danny's salon.

.....

I've always been an avid, quick reader but that didn't equate with being a good learner. At school I developed some kind of mental block and for many years I just couldn't get things to stick.

These days I can get through trashy fiction novels in a single sitting but I've pretty much forgotten them within a couple of days. They're distractions, that's all; something to pass the time. But when I read something that really catches my imagination I take my time over it, poring over every sentence; every word. I become totally engrossed in the story so that when I next pick up the book again I am able to slip straight back into it. Eventually details start to fade so I re-read my favourite books over and over again. I've done that now to the point that I could quote whole passages from some of them. Chunks of fictional characters' lives stay vividly in my mind and yet there are whole periods of my own life that are a blank.

.....

That first summer at Danny's, he and my mother went for a long weekend to the coast. I wasn't part of their plans and, for a while, there was talk of me going to stay with Grandma and Grandpa. For the first time since we'd left Manning Road I dared to hope that I might soon see Dadda again. In the end Danny decided the detour was too far and would eat into their holiday time so I ended up staying with Colin and Eileen. Over the five days and four nights of my stay with them I came out of my shell a bit, especially with Susan, Colin and Eileen's eldest daughter. She was two years older than me and liked to read as well, so we swapped books. She was one of the best readers in her class and was impressed that I could read as well as her.

A gang of kids knocked about in the streets around Colin and Eileen's house in much the same way as the kids on Manning Road. With Susan's encouragement I joined in their games and even started to enjoy playing with other kids again. Unfortunately the experience was short-lived. As soon as my mother and Danny returned it was back to the flat, the yard, the library and my own company.

By the time I started back at Sacred Heart I had developed a kind of inner strength from spending so much time on my own. Not confidence exactly; more a kind of self-sufficiency. I found I was able to ignore the taunts in the playground. I could stand and take them rather than running and hiding. When the kids realised they could no longer get to me they gave up and found new targets.

While I still had nightmares and wet the bed occasionally I no longer suffered the indignity and embarrassment of wetting myself in class. I kept myself pretty much to myself and as time went on I was grudgingly accepted; if not included. I was quite content to spend playtimes with a book. Occasionally I might join some of the other outcasts in the playground but I never made any close friends. Not like Simon and David had been at St. Mike's.

And that was the pattern of my four and a half years at Sacred Heart. I was a below-average pupil with a reputation for being quiet and having poor concentration. It surprised no one when I failed the eleven plus examination.

.....

Although my time at Sacred Heart wasn't particularly enjoyable, it wasn't one long period of unremitting misery. I can't, with honesty, recall many moments that I would describe as really happy or joyful but most of the time, once things had settled down, life there was bearable.

I was a serious little boy but that doesn't mean I didn't have a sense of humour. I did and, while I didn't laugh very often, I found things to smile at. I like to think of myself at such times as having a gentle gleam in my eyes. Like Dadda used to have.

.....

"There's an occasional twinkle behind that grim facade of yours," Tom once commented. "Sometimes I wonder what's going on in that head."

"That makes two of us," I replied.

.....

There is one incident from my time at Sacred Heart that I do remember fondly. It happened in the summer term when I was in the third year juniors.

I was hidden away in the shrubs at the top end of the playground, reading a book. I was so engrossed in the story that I didn't hear the bell ring for the end of lunch break. The other kids had already lined up and gone back into class when I heard my name being called. As I got to my feet I heard something moving in the bushes a few yards to my left. Suddenly a fox shot out of its cover and ran towards Mrs. Hickey, one of the dinner ladies, who was standing about twenty yards away in the middle of the playground. As soon as it saw her it turned sharply and crossed a few yards in front of me. It was the first time I'd ever seen a live, wild fox. I was struck by the sleekness of it, the brilliance of its red coat and the stealth of its movement. It quickly disappeared back into bushes and bolted through a gap in the fence.

"Did you see that, Mason?" Mrs. Hickey asked as she walked over to me.

I liked Mrs. Hickey. She was a softer version of Grandma and always had a pack of small kids hanging from her hands and clinging to her coat at break times.

"It was lovely, Miss," I replied. "Where did it come from?"

"I've no idea. It's not often you see a fox in the daytime, Mason. Especially in the middle of town. He must have been sniffing around the bins."

"Was he hungry?" I asked.

"I should think so. Something's driven it to roam around in broad daylight like that. Poor thing."

"Maybe I could save some of my dinner for it tomorrow, Miss?" I suggested.

"You shouldn't really encourage them, Mason. And if Mr. Price (the caretaker) knew about it he'd as like to give it poison as give it food. If it manages to get a bit of something around the back of the kitchen, then good luck to it. But I think we should keep this a secret, Mason. For the old fox's sake."

"All right, Miss," I agreed.

And I did keep it a secret. To the best of my knowledge the only people who ever knew about the fox were Mrs. Hickey and I.

.....

I sometimes see foxes while I'm at work. It's usually in the evening although I have occasionally seen them during the day; but that's very rare. And there have been a few times when I've heard the squeals of a rabbit being taken by a fox. That's nature. Death is as much a part of it as life. And that's something Dadda understood.

.....

While I was at Sacred Heart I made my first confession, received First Holy Communion and was confirmed; all of the major milestones in the development of a young Catholic.

My mother didn't live a particularly devout lifestyle but she did take me to mass on Sundays and she seemed keen that I was introduced properly into the Catholic faith. I assume this was to keep my grandparents happy.

At confession I used to make up sins because I couldn't think of any real ones I'd committed.

"Bless me father for I have sinned, it is two weeks since my last confession, here are my sins: I stole some money from my mother's purse (not true); I said a bad word (not true); I kicked the neighbour's cat (definitely not true); and I wished my mother was dead when she shouted at me (probably true)."

The one thing I hardly ever admitted to was telling lies, which was precisely what I did every time I went into the confessional.

In the early days of making my confession I used to offer up my penance - rarely more than a couple of Hail Mary's, an Our Father and an Act Of Contrition – as though my life depended on it. As I got older and more cynical my list of made-up sins became more extreme and I used to try to work out what prayer, or multiples thereof, equated to what sin. It all seemed pretty random to me and I soon stopped bothering with the penance.

The significance of the sacrament of Holy Communion was impressed on us again and again; we were taking Jesus' body, in the form of the host, into our mouths; into our bodies. But the thing I remember most about receiving communion is how self-conscious I felt walking up the aisle to the altar and, even more so, on my way back with the wafer of bread resting on my tongue. Or, more often than not, glued to the roof of my mouth. When I got back to my place in the pew I would kneel and stare at the altar or the round stained-glass window, trying to peel one third of the Holy Trinity off my palate with the tip of my tongue while I waited for some sign or revelation.

Confirmation is the 'rite that admits a baptized person to full church membership'. (I had to look that up in my dictionary because I'd forgotten what it was all about.) The only thing I do remember about the ritual is taking the name of a saint to whom I was supposed to pray for guidance and help. A kind of guardian angel. Most kids took the names of the better-known saints: St. Francis of Assissi, St. Peter or St. Christopher who carried the infant Jesus across the river. I chose my confirmation name, Stephen, for obvious reasons.

4

For the first few months in Danny's flat my mother refused to talk about Dadda. When I asked when we'd be seeing him she told me bluntly that we wouldn't be seeing him; this was our new life and it had nothing to do with him and that was an end to it. Either that or my questions were met with a wall of silence. In the end I stopped asking.

My grandparents didn't have the telephone installed back then so my mother and Grandma kept in touch by mail. For three years my mother never let me see any of Grandma's letters, so I never knew if there was any mention of Dadda in them. By the time I did get my hands on one it was too late. A fact that I'm sure was not coincidental.

I was doing some dusting and polishing in the lounge when my mother came upstairs with the post.

"Letter from your Grandma," she announced, flopping onto the sofa. She ripped open the envelope and picked up her cup of tea from the coffee table.

Under normal circumstances she'd glance over the letter, read aloud any bits that were of interest or relevance to me then put it back in the envelope. After which it would not be seen again. I think she used to keep them with her and throw them away somewhere where I could never find them. However, on this occasion she cast her eye over the letter, threw it down onto the sofa, drained her cup and announced pointedly that she was going down to the salon and wouldn't be back for at least ten minutes. I wasn't sure if it was an invitation or a challenge and I hesitated for a minute or two after she'd gone.

Did I expect to find any mention of Dadda in the letter? I don't remember. There was no reason why I should have done; on the evidence of what my mother had read to me over the previous three years he had never been mentioned before.

Grandma's handwriting wasn't easy to read and it was a slow process trying to decipher it. There was news of my mother's siblings and their families. There was an update of my grandparents' debate about whether or not they should join the trend and build an extension onto the back of the house: Grandpa was in favour, Grandma didn't see why they needed one. It was just more money and she was quite happy with the way things were. (Today most of the houses on Manning Road have extensions.) Grandma had bought herself two lovely second-hand summer dresses from the St. Vincent de Paul shop. And there was a paragraph of the usual gossip about the neighbours and people at church, at the end of which I read the following sentence:

'Stephen finally heard from his brother in Australia. He's sold the house and gone.'

And that was that. The first hard facts I'd seen or heard about Dadda in over three years was the news that he had disappeared to Australia. Even with my rudimentary knowledge of geography I knew that Australia was on the other side of the world. He might as well have been on a different planet.

Up until that moment there had been times when I dreamed of running away and trying to find him; that dream was shattered now. Dadda had gone and, what was worse, he hadn't come to rescue me as I had so often wished and prayed he would. My guardian angel had deserted me; although I didn't blame him.

I put the letter back on the sofa and went to my room. I thought I might cry but I didn't. After a few minutes staring out of the window I picked up the book I was reading, lay on my bed and, as I so often did, I found solace in a different world; a different life.

.....

In later years my mother told me Grandma had mentioned Dadda in her letters. She said she hadn't told me at the time because she thought it would make it more difficult for me to settle into our new life with Danny. That it would upset me. She tried to make out she had done it for my own good. The sad thing is, I think she actually believed it.

I heard more about Dadda's emigration when I went back to live with Grandma and Grandpa.

In the early nineteen fifties Dadda's younger brother, Ted, joined the merchant navy. After a couple of postcards from his first voyage nothing was heard of him for almost ten years. Then, out of the blue in the early nineteen sixties Nanna received a letter from him. He had met a woman in Sydney, they had married and he was settling down over there. There then followed another lengthy silence.

Over two and a half years after I was taken away from Manning Road Nanna had another, more severe stroke. Realising she might not have long to live Dadda wrote to Ted at his last known address saying he should come home quickly if he wanted to see Nanna before she died. As it turned out she went quite suddenly and Ted's reply came two days after the funeral. He said he couldn't afford to come back to England on short notice, for which he apologised, and he ended his letter with an open invitation for Dadda to join him out in Sydney.

Once the funeral was out of the way (Nanna was cremated) Dadda telegraphed Ted to make sure his offer was genuine. When he received a positive reply he put 163 on the market, completed the sale of the house, bought his ticket, packed his bags and left, all within a period of two months. Grandma reckoned if he could have done it quicker he would have. She said that once Nanna had died there was nothing to keep him in Manning Road. He had become distant and uncommunicative. Reclusive almost. He didn't even go for a pint with Grandpa any more.

A couple of years later my mother gave me a different version of events. According to her, Dadda stopped talking to Grandma and Grandpa not long after we left when they repeatedly refused to give him our address or pass on his letters to me.

.....

When Dadda was preparing to go to Australia he gave Big Mick the pick of his tools and anything else he wanted from the house before he sold the contents. He also entrusted him with the carving of the castle and one other special piece, both of which Big Mick promised to pass on to me if I ever returned to Manning Road. Unfortunately three years later Mick and his wife decided to move away as well. Wanting to keep his promise he reasoned that if I was ever going to get the carvings the best chance would be to leave them with

Grandma and Grandpa, to whom he hadn't spoken since I was taken away.

Big Mick wasn't called Big Mick for nothing. He went around to my grandparents' house and, by all accounts, made it quite clear to Grandpa that he was now responsible for passing on the carvings to me. And that if he heard Grandpa had failed there would be trouble. Apparently there was very little argument.

This was another incident my grandparents neglected to mention in their account of events in Manning Road.

5

I have one particular memory concerning Danny. The occasion was an unfortunate one although, in the long run, it turned out all right.

In the summer holidays before my final year at Sacred Heart my mother, Danny and I went to a Butlins camp for a week. They liked it there because they could sign me up for all the kids' activities and then forget about me while they enjoyed the various adult pursuits, most of which took place in or near the bar.

Anyway, as the three of us were walking past the swimming pool one day Danny asked me if I could swim. When I told him I couldn't he said:

"You can't? I tell you what; I'll take you when we get back home. It'll be a nice change instead of moping around the flat or locking yourself away down the library."

I didn't think too much about it at the time as he was quite drunk but a couple of weeks later, true to his word, he told me to get my swimming stuff as we were going to the local baths. I've a fair idea it was at a time he and my mother were having one of their many bad patches so he was probably doing it to humour her. Not that I cared.

I remember the crash of noise as we walked through the double swing doors from the ticket office into the pool: kids screaming and splashing and whistling and howling. Everything amplified as it echoed around the building. It was like a madhouse. I'd never been to a public baths before so this was a whole new experience for me.

The depth of the pool dropped in a steady gradient from three feet down to six feet and for the first ten or fifteen minutes Danny gave me some tuition in the shallow end: getting me to hang on to the bar at the side and kick my legs; holding me under my stomach while I windmilled my arms ineffectually; trying to get me floating on my back. However he soon got restless and went for a swim, striking out for the deep end where a bevy of young women were clinging to the side, gossiping.

While he was gone I tried a few more leg kicks but soon bored of the exercise. I squatted against one of the circular heaters at the end of the pool and watched the other kids. I realised a lot of them didn't appear to be particularly good swimmers but were still throwing themselves around fearlessly, having a great time. I had no desire to join in with their games but I longed to have their confidence. I knew I would enjoy swimming once I'd learned how. I had always liked water. I especially liked the way it distorts sound. When I had baths I used to tilt back my head to submerge my ears, then close my eyes and let the gentle underwater white noise wash over me. Even at that young age I wondered if that might be what death sounded like.

After a few minutes Danny came back to see how I was getting on. He got me to hold onto the bar and have another go at the front crawl stroke, suggesting I practise this for a couple of minutes before pushing myself away from the side while keeping my arms going. And off he went to hang around in the deep end again.

Now that I can swim I understand what he was trying to tell me; he just didn't explain himself very clearly. At the time I did what I thought he meant, which was to hang onto the bar, push off backwards and try to swim back to the side. Which didn't work in the shallow water because as soon as I lost my backward momentum my legs sank and I stood up. I decided I needed to be in deeper water so that my feet wouldn't reach the bottom and hamper me. I went to the five feet mark and looked around again at the other kids happily swimming, floating and treading water. It looked so easy. I held myself at arm's length from the bar, swung my arms a few times and pushed away from the side.

There was an exhilarating moment when I thought I was

swimming, quickly followed by the realisation that I was going nowhere except down. Panic set in. I twisted in the water, looking around me, grasping for something to hang onto. As I sank I screamed but the sound was lost in the muted reverberating din of the pool. I saw the bubbles rise like mercury from my mouth. I saw the bright colours of swimming costumes, limbs like bleached wood, white plumes of foam as bodies entered the water, the aquamarine tiles below and to the sides of me, the undulating image of the glass roof of the building above me. The commotion seemed to go on for ages while I got weaker and more sluggish until, for no reason I can explain, I was filled with a sense of tranquillity and I stopped struggling. I hung in the water, relaxed and pleasantly limp, free from worry and fear. I felt totally at peace. The next thing I knew I'd floated to the surface, gulped a lungful of air and the fight for survival resumed. I thrashed about, throwing out an arm, snatching instinctively for life. I scraped a fingernail down the side of the pool and brushed a fingertip across a fleshy back before I got a firm grip on a dangling leg and dragged myself back to the safety of the bar.

Coughing and spluttering I pulled myself along the rail to the steps at the shallow end. Choking, crying and shivering I sat on a poolside bench, wanting someone to hold me and tell me it was all right. Wanting to be wrapped in a strong, comforting embrace.

When Danny came back from flirting in the deep end and I explained what had happened he was clearly shocked. We got dressed immediately and went to the pool cafeteria where he bought me a hot chocolate and a marshmallow biscuit. Sitting at a table next to a radiator I warmed my hands on the hot mug while Danny, ridden with guilt, begged me not to tell my mother what had happened.

"I'm sorry, Mason, I should have kept an eye on you. I don't suppose you'll want to go swimming again in a hurry, will you?" he asked.

I thought about watching the other kids in the pool. I thought about the moment of serenity I had experienced. I thought about that feeling of suspended, floating freedom as I rose to the surface and, much to Danny's surprise, I asked if we could go again the following week.

At last I had found an activity I was interested in. I quickly learned how to swim and before too long I was going to the baths on my own. It was the only vaguely sporting activity I ever enjoyed. And I continue to enjoy it to this day.

.....

One of the many jobs I have had over the years was working as a lifeguard in a public swimming pool. The only requirement was that I was a strong swimmer, as I received on-the-job training to get my bronze medallion life-saving award. During the eight months I held the job I never once had to go into the water to save anyone; never had to use either of the two towing techniques I was taught, of which the cross-chest tow was my preferred choice. Apart from when I was training I have only ever used that towing method once and it wasn't to save a life.

6

When we first moved in with Danny, his flat looked like a bomb had hit it. My mother lived with that state of affairs for a few days, until Christmas was out of the way and she had found her feet, at which point she started changing things to her liking. It wasn't long before she had Danny scrubbing, mopping, polishing and dusting. She even did her share to begin with. She was determined to make the place hers − a new broom sweeping clean - and this was the first step. I was roped in to help as well - with Danny trying to turn the task into a kind of game to keep me interested − and we soon had the place looking spick and span. The next trick for my mother was to keep it like that without having to do too much work herself. She constantly complained and badgered us about cleanliness and tidiness. Apparently she was never responsible for any mess in the place; it was always my fault or Danny's and we were expected to deal with it.

.....

This was the first time I'd really seen this overbearing, bullying side to my mother.

Back in Manning Road she wouldn't have dared throw her weight around with Grandma or Grandpa. She might sulk or have the odd tantrum but she would never push it too far, especially once they'd made a stand. And, despite her lack of concern for Dadda's feelings when it came to her extra-marital activities, I think she realised she had an obligation to respect him and his standards in his own home. After all, when he married her he had given up a lot and received little in return.

In Danny's flat she didn't have that sense of obligation. She probably thought she was doing him a favour. I have no idea what Danny was like before he knew my mother; I imagine him to have been a confident, successful, go-getting sort of person. But over the five years we lived with him my mother gradually wore him down, treating him increasingly like a menial. More gofer than go-getter.

To an extent he brought it on himself. When they first met he was obviously completely besotted with my mother and eager to please her. He set the tone of their relationship by always doing things for her – running errands, buying her gifts, fulfilling her whims – as many new lovers do. She of course took full advantage of this, without too much reciprocation that I ever saw. When his enthusiasm to make her happy started to fade she still got her own way, using a combination of threats, verbal and physical violence and sexual provocation. He stood up to her from time to time but didn't have the backbone to see it through.

.....

My mother met Danny at a wedding where she was a bridesmaid, he was best man and I should have been pageboy. On the morning of the wedding I was left at home while my mother jumped into the taxi taking her to the bride's parents' house. She told everybody that I had come down with a fever. I didn't mind because I didn't particularly want to get dressed up in the hideous burgundy suit and claret bowtie I was supposed to wear. And I got to go out for the day with Dadda instead.

Of course, my mother didn't want me there because she didn't want to have to look after me. She had already heard a lot about Danny, the groom's cousin. She knew all about his good looks, his charm and his money. As soon as the ceremony was over she made a beeline for him so she could get her claws into him before anyone else did. She has bragged since that, even before she met him, she had decided Danny was going to be her meal ticket to take her away from Dadda's house.

In true clichéd style the best man got off with the bridesmaid. And it didn't take them long to consummate their union either.

"Standing up in the back yard of the pub surrounded by beer barrels and empty crates. Very romantic," my mother used to tease Danny sometimes.

At first those taunts were gentle and good-natured but by the end they had become bitter and sarcastic. What she always failed to mention was that it was she who instigated the whole thing.

.....

My mother was a hard woman. In the eighteen years I lived with her I don't remember ever seeing her cry, apart from crocodile tears, which she could turn on like a tap when it suited her. In fact, if I had to compare her to an animal it would have to be a crocodile; thick skinned and cold blooded.

Danny didn't have a chance with her. And he never stopped loving her. Despite their fights; despite his suspicions and fears about her fidelity; despite having those suspicions confirmed; despite the fact that she ridiculed him, belittled him and eventually pushed him to the point where he couldn't control himself any longer and hit her across the face – an action he immediately regretted and for which he begged forgiveness; despite everything she did to him, when she told him she was leaving he still wanted her to stay. Was this a further display of his weakness? Or was it more a display of the influence my mother held over men? I don't know. Whatever the case it didn't matter anyway; after five years with Danny my mother was looking for a reason to leave him and the slap across the face gave her that reason. She had already met Roger and decided the two of us were going off with him. In another clichéd gesture we ran away with a travelling salesman.

7

Roger was an idiot. I struggle to think of anyone I have ever met who could match his level of stupidity. He was good at his job, possibly because of his open, friendly nature; but paradoxically perhaps for a salesman, he was easily deceived.

When he met my mother, who was several years his junior, he was happily married with two children. He was plain and boring and had a safe, comfortable life living in a semi-detached house. My mother was young, wild, attractive and oozing sexuality, which he found tremendously exciting. She soon had him dangling on a thread. Within weeks of Danny hitting her Roger had moved us to his hometown and into a small rented flat that he had procured and paid for.

For the next nine months my mother was a kept woman. She got a job but allowed Roger to continue paying our rent and helping out with the bills. In return for this he came around one or two evenings a week and stayed the night. On her nights off she went out and met other men, sometimes bringing them back to the flat or staying out until the following morning. All of which Roger was blissfully unaware of. For my mother this was the perfect arrangement; it was only when Roger started talking about leaving his wife and kids to move in with us that she decided things were getting out of hand. One Saturday morning we packed our things, loaded them into the back of an old van belonging to one of her men friends and he drove us to the council maisonette my mother had secured for us on a local estate. And that was that.

Poor Roger probably never knew what hit him. She gave him no warning and didn't contact him afterwards. I imagine him turning up one Tuesday or Wednesday night, armed with his usual present of chocolates or flowers or a bottle of gin, letting himself into his little love nest, announcing his arrival in that irritating, playful voice and walking expectantly into an empty flat. Not even a note. Maybe I should feel sorry for him (I can even feel a touch of sympathy for Danny) but I don't. The man was a fool. Which is why my mother chose him.

8

About six months before we left Danny I started attending the St. Paul The Apostle Secondary School. This was after I'd had to repeat my final year at Sacred Heart because of an administrative error when I went to St. Mike's. Apparently I was admitted a year earlier than I should have been, an error that the authorities failed to pick up when I transferred to Sacred Heart. The mistake wasn't noticed until I was registered for the eleven plus which, despite having two years to study for, I still managed to fail.

I don't remember much about those two terms at St. Paul's except that that was where I was first taught woodwork, the only subject in which I ever really excelled. I can recall the tingle of excitement as I walked into the workshop and put on my apron; the smell of sawdust and freshly cut wood; the pleasure of handling the tools. The first thing I ever made was a paper knife, shaped with a spoke shave and finished lovingly with fine sandpaper. I got an A+ for it. I rarely scored less than an A for anything I produced in woodwork classes.

While it's possible that my flair for woodwork was natural it's more likely that it came as a result of the associations it had with Dadda. It served as a constant reminder, making me feel somehow close to him; as a result of which I worked hard at it, striving to achieve the feel for and understanding of wood that he had possessed.

.....

During the time we lived in Roger's flat and in the maisonette I went to Holy Souls Secondary School, where I continued to shine in woodwork and where an English teacher, Mr. Flowers, picked up on my love of reading. He used to recommend books to me and even lent me some of his own. One of these was Tolkien's *Lord Of The Rings*, a book which reminded me of some of Dadda's stories and, as a consequence, is a favourite that I have read several times. Mr. Flowers also encouraged me to express myself in creative writing and I started turning out stories which, although grammatically weak, were strong in imagination. Fortunately he was in favour of rewarding content as much as style and I received some good marks. So now I had two lessons I enjoyed.

When puberty arrived I was one of the first to grow pubic hair and found myself the butt of the joke in the showers after PE and games. However, once most of the other boys had started sprouting hair things calmed down and I was left alone again.

At the age of fourteen I still had the occasional nightmare but I had long since stopped wetting the bed. So I was very surprised and not a little concerned when I woke up one morning to find a damp patch on the sheet and stickiness on my belly and groin. It took me a while to realise what had happened. In the playground I had noticed the changing nature of relationships between the boys and girls in my year but I don't remember having any carnal thoughts about anyone. Obviously somewhere in the depths of my sleeping subconscious things were stirring.

. . . . .

Life with my mother in Roger's flat and the maisonette was more relaxed than when we were with Danny.

We had a simple routine: I went to school, came home and did my homework. She went to work, came home and had a gin. We took it in turns to cook and usually ate together at the dinner table where our conversations tended to be fairly superficial, discussing household matters or telling one another about our respective days. Then we'd clear up and if she wasn't going out I might sit with her and watch the television that had been bought for us by Roger. ('The Doormat' as she called him.) Or I might read in my room or go for a wander through the streets. We did most of the cleaning at weekends – or rather, I did, for which I received pocket money – and, other than that, we lived our lives almost totally independent of each other.

I don't remember us ever fighting or arguing throughout that whole period.

.....

In the eleven years I spent with my mother after we left Manning Road the softness of her looks faded in direct relation to the hardening of her personality, but I suppose she was still a good-looking woman. She was more angular and severe-looking, becoming skinny rather than slim as a result of her smoking, but she was still attractive to men. And she knew it.

Of the various men she brought back to Roger's flat and the maisonette few appeared more than a couple of times. One or two became friends rather than lovers but, in the main, she seemed happier keeping things casual. So I was quite surprised when she started seeing Andy on a regular basis. Even more surprised when, to the best of my knowledge, she stopped sleeping with other men. That smacked of commitment, not exactly her strong suit.

Andy was the only one of my mother's many boyfriends that I actually quite liked, despite his insistence on calling me 'Mace'. He was more intelligent than the others and didn't let my mother walk all over him like Roger and Danny had. He was a decent guy who showed enough interest in me – without being at all condescending in the way Roger had – to encourage me to want to talk to him.

As a structural engineer he had worked abroad several times before, so going to the Middle East was no big deal for him. Quite why he arranged to take my mother with him I don't know. He obviously liked her but, as on the day of my fourteenth birthday, there were occasions when I saw him squirm uncomfortably at some of the things she did or said.

.....

It was Andy who recognised my interest in photography and bought me my second camera, which was a combined late birthday and Christmas present.

I had eventually got a film for Dadda's camera and started taking photographs when I was eleven. The first reel stayed in the camera for over a year before I got it developed. I remember thinking it was like a little time capsule and being very excited when I got the pictures back because I'd completely forgotten what I'd photographed. They were mainly snaps of things around Danny's flat and many were out of focus or underexposed. I threw most of them away at some time or another but I did keep two, which I still have. One is of Danny's hanging chair, in which I found comfort on that first Christmas away from Dadda. The other is a photograph of my own feet taken, I think, in the yard behind the salon. This is possibly an unusual shot for an eleven-year-old to have taken but it set a trend which I kept up for many years: photographing my feet against various backgrounds, some abstract, some recognisable. At one time in my teens, when I fancied myself as an avant-garde photographer, I had an ambition of putting on an exhibition or publishing a book with this as the theme. I was going to call it 'Feet Accompli'. Nothing came of the idea. Which is a shame because I didn't have too many other ambitions when I was growing up.

The camera Andy gave me was a good one and still works today. Not that I ever take photographs these days. I still have Dadda's camera too but that hasn't worked for years. I've hung onto it because it's the last thing he ever gave me.

.....

My mother was understandably excited about going to the Middle East, not least because she had never even been out of England before, let alone the British Isles. Andy made all the arrangements for her; organising her passport and visa and sorting out a job for her to go to. He even helped her pack, advising her on what type of clothes would be best to cope with the heat and local customs.

My packing for going to Grandma and Grandpa's was pretty straightforward. Apart from clothes I only had a few belongings I wanted to take, the important ones being Dadda's camera, my first photograph album and a couple of things I'd made in woodwork.

My mother arranged for a friend to move into the maisonette

while we were away so we'd have somewhere to come back to. And also to keep her name on the council list. She had quickly learned all of the scams and loopholes you needed to know if you were living in a council property.

Two days before Christmas Eve we piled into Andy's car and drove away from the estate. In the seven years since we left Manning Road we'd never once been back, we hadn't seen Grandma and Grandpa and I'd only spoken to them a handful of times. It was a weird feeling to be heading back there again, not knowing what to expect, wondering if it would be like I remembered it.

Sitting in a roadside café, struggling to eat a sausage sandwich, I gazed out of the window and thought about my life in Manning Road with Dadda. My stomach was churning and I had a lump in my throat. For the first time in a long while I felt as though I might cry. I put the sandwich down on my plate.

"You all right, Mace?" asked Andy.

"I'm just not very hungry," I replied.

"He's probably just excited about seeing his Grandma and Grandpa again, aren't you Mason?" my mother suggested.

I nodded and smiled weakly. She had no idea.

9

Grandma and Grandpa couldn't believe how big I'd got.

"We'll be having to get a bigger bed for you, Mason," Grandpa observed. "He's practically a grown man, Grandma."

I took my things up to the front bedroom, which was to be my room for the next seven months.

(Grandma had won the argument over the extension, so the bathroom was still upstairs and I had to go through their bedroom to get to it. On several occasions I startled Grandpa out of a deep sleep as I crept to the loo in the middle of the night.

"What!? Who!? Who's there? What?!" he'd shout in confusion before realising what was happening. "Oh, it's you, Mason. OK. Don't be flushing the chain. You'll wake up the whole street." And he'd roll over and go back to sleep.)

That night my mother and Andy – who had a cool reception from my grandparents – stayed in a local bed and breakfast. It was unthinkable that they should sleep together, out of wedlock, under Grandma's roof. The next day they returned and had lunch with us before heading off to the airport. As a special surprise Andy had arranged for them to spend Christmas in Austria with a friend of his. They would fly on to the Middle East from there. So this was 'goodbye'.

"You want to put a bit of weight on you. And you should stop that smoking," Grandma chastised my mother before softening. "We see you for two minutes after seven years and you're off again," she added as she hugged her and said farewell.

"You take good care of her now," Grandpa warned Andy, gripping his hand with extra pressure to make his point.

"We'll be fine," my mother told him with mild irritation. "I'll write and let you know how we're getting on. We'll be back for a break before the year's out, anyway."

"You've only a week to go then," Grandpa joked.

As I lurked in the background, wishing they'd get on with it and go, Andy came over and patted me on the shoulder.

"See you, Mace. Once we get settled in we'll see about you joining us. Yeah?"

I nodded as he smiled encouragingly before slipping past Grandpa and out of the front door.

I thought for a moment that my mother was going to leave without saying goodbye to me but she turned in the doorway.

"Bye, Mason. Behave yourself, OK? I've left you some pocket money with Grandma. I'll send you more when we get paid." Then, almost as an afterthought: "Have a nice Christmas."

"You too," I replied. "And a safe trip."

"I can't wait," she bubbled and hurried out to Andy's car.

That evening, after tea, I went for a wander around the area. I turned left at the bottom of the entry and walked to Astor Road where I stood for a while, leaning over the wall of St. Mike's playground. Then I cut down one of the cross streets onto Rufus Road and back onto Manning Road. As I approached 163 I didn't know if I wanted to walk past quickly or stop for a good look. The front door had been painted a different colour and there was litter in the front garden. I had an urge to tidy it up, just as Dadda had tidied the Lauras' grave, but I stopped myself. Memories flooded back and I tried to think only of the good, happy things but I wasn't able to block out feelings of sadness. I didn't want to go back to Grandma and Grandpa's yet so I did another slow circuit around the block, unmindful of the fact that my mother had just gone away but feeling acutely the loss of Dadda.

.....

On Christmas Eve I went to confession with Grandma and on Christmas Day we went to mass. After breakfast I had a handful of presents to open: the camera from Andy, which was a very pleasant surprise; a penknife and a woolly hat from my mother; and a card with a two pound postal order from Grandma and Grandpa.

"We didn't know what you liked so we thought you could get yourself something," explained Grandma.

I thanked them and was about to go into the kitchen to start peeling potatoes for dinner when Grandpa suddenly exclaimed:

"Oh! I nearly forgot. There's something else for you in the front room. In the alcove by the window. It's not wrapped but I think you'll know what it is."

Grandma looked at him questioningly for a second before she realised what he was talking about.

"Oh, yes, Mason! A little surprise for you," she said with a significant raise of her eyebrows.

I went into the front room and saw the castle immediately. I took it down from the high shelf it was standing on, sat myself in an armchair and placed it carefully on my lap. Running my hands over it I remembered the day it was finished, when Dadda gave it a final rub with sandpaper and called me over to the shed step to show it to me.

"Your Dadda left it with us before he went off to Australia," Grandpa lied. "I promised we'd give it back to you and there it is!"

Meanwhile Grandma had got down on her hands and knees by the sideboard and, after a bit of rummaging, emerged from the depths of one of its cupboards.

"Here's another one," she said, handing me something wrapped in a soft cloth. "Now I have to get on with the dinner."

She and Grandpa went back to the kitchen and living room respectively, leaving me alone to open the bundle. There was another carving inside. I laid it in the palm of one hand and ran my fingertips over its surface. It was glass smooth and had obviously received special care and attention in its making. It was the face of a young boy, turned at a slight angle to the left: chubby round cheeks; thin lips; chin like the pointed end of an egg; curls of hair; and inquiring, attentive eyes. My mother never owned a camera and never asked to use mine so I'd seen very few photographs of myself as a child. It is no surprise then that it took some time for me to realise that the face I was looking at was my own. I have no idea why my grandparents had hidden it away in a cupboard. It is a beautiful piece.

10

Over the next few months I explored the area I had started growing up in.

About half a mile beyond Rufus Road I found the park I used to go to with Dadda. Things hadn't changed much. The old metal swings, slides and roundabout had been replaced with a robust-looking wood-and-rope adventure playground. The areas of shrubbery were denser. The rail around the bandstand in the centre of the park had been smashed in a couple of places, leaving dangerous rusty jags of iron sticking out. The pool had been drained and turned into a flowerbed. Otherwise it was pretty much as I remembered it. Although, in the evenings, I got the sense that it wasn't a safe place to be, despite the patrolling wardens.

There were a few days during the winter when snow covered the sledging hill, but it was never as magical as it had been on that wonderful Christmas morning. How could it have been without Dadda there?

In the opposite direction to the park, beyond Astor Road, I came across St. Angela's church and cemetery, the place I would one day come to work. Back then I didn't know anyone buried there. Today I could go and visit the graves of Grandpa and Michael if I chose but I don't bother, except in the course of my duties.

The first time I went there was on a still sombre day with a slate grey sky, which added to the atmosphere of the place. I appreciated this because it reflected my own mood and because, for various reasons, it reminded me of Dadda: his melancholic nature and his aura of peace and calm. I found myself drifting among the headstones, reading the inscriptions, watching strangers tending graves or lost in contemplation beside them, and I was reminded of visiting the Lauras' grave with Dadda. I spent quite some time there on that first occasion and as I wandered I was also reminded, for the first time in years, of the gravedigger. I wondered what had become of him. When I got back to Grandma and Grandpa's house I asked if they remembered him but they didn't seem to know whom I was talking about.

A couple of months later, when I'd got to know Stan, the gravedigger at St. Angela's at the time, I asked if he knew anything about the gravedigger of my childhood but he didn't remember him either.

During the seven months my mother was in Saudia Arabia I took to visiting St. Angela's on a regular basis. Most of the time I was content to wander about on my own but there were occasions when I'd sit at the back of the chapel during a funeral service or watch a burial from an unobtrusive distance.

I don't know why I got into the habit of going to the cemetery. Even now I can't explain it. Maybe I saw it as the one place I could be guaranteed peace and quiet; where I would be left alone. Maybe that was it. That was certainly one of the reasons for my returning there to work fourteen years later.

.....

"You're very quiet, Mason," Grandpa pointed out soon after I moved in with them. "You used to be such a lively little boy. Full of laughs. Isn't that right Grandma?"

"Laugh a minute, you were," she assured me over the clack-clack-clack of her knitting needles. "I was always after chasing you up the garden for sticking your nose up against the window there. Do you remember?"

I shrugged and smiled and shook my head.

"He's turned into a thinker, that's what he has," said Grandpa, taking a drag from his roll-up. "Just like his Dadda."

"The Quiet Man. John Wayne," Grandma added enthusiastically.

"Now that's a great film," Grandpa agreed. "Maureen O'Hara. Did you ever see it, Mason?"

I shook my head again.

"A great film," he confirmed.

I smiled and returned to the book I was reading.

.....

I had long since lost any religious beliefs I may have had but I still went to mass with my mother and continued to do so with my grandparents. However, I stopped short of going to confession, although they didn't know that. They thought I went on a Saturday evening after cleaning windows but, while Grandpa watched the racing results on television and Grandma prepared the tea, I'd go up to St. Mike's and just hang around outside for a while before going back home.

"You were quick, Mason!"

"There wasn't a queue, Grandma," I'd explain.

"Aah, it's terrible," she'd reply. "There's an awful lot of people out there with sins and secrets who aren't being true to themselves. Or to Our Lord."

Pots and kettles.

.....

The nearest Catholic secondary school, The Oratory, was a bus ride away. During the two terms I spent there I continued to show ability in woodwork and creative writing. There was an

107

improvement in my understanding of grammar and language that, in turn, helped me develop more of an interest in English Literature as well.

Two evenings a week it was possible to stay on after school finished and use the library for doing homework. I always took advantage of these sessions to study or to read my own books in peace, away from Grandma's constant chatter and demands for me to run errands or help her with housework. It wasn't so much that I minded doing jobs for her, it was more the fact that she kept going on about how quiet I'd become. Was it because of Andy? Or Danny? Or what was it? I'd just shrug and say I didn't know.

.....

Not long after Easter I was beaten up a second time.

About two weeks beforehand I'd discovered that the cemetery where the Lauras were buried was only twenty minutes' walk from school and I decided I'd try to find their grave.

On the morning of the day in question I told Grandma I'd be home late, saying I was going into town to the central library to look for some books I needed. I don't know why but I didn't want her to know where I was really going.

At the cemetery I immediately recognised the main gate but beyond that I didn't have a clue where the grave might be. Still, it was a pleasant evening and I was quite content to search among the headstones. Three hours later I was surprised to see that the light was fading and to realise how much time had passed. I hadn't found the Lauras but I'd covered one section of the cemetery fairly thoroughly and I reasoned that I'd be able to gradually narrow things down with a methodical approach on future visits.

Although my mental map of the area wasn't particularly detailed I knew that walking back to school and then getting the bus back to Grandma and Grandpa's would be taking two sides of a triangle, so I decided to find a more direct route on foot. As I walked through the unfamiliar streets I was filled with a sense of adventure, imagining myself as an intrepid explorer striding across uncharted territories.

I had just passed a small row of shops and started to descend a steep hill when I heard footsteps and voices catching up behind me. I wasn't unduly concerned by this as it was still quite light and I was on a residential street. The two older boys came alongside and one of them spoke to me. I couldn't make out what he was saying and, thinking I hadn't heard properly, I mumbled something and shrugged. He repeated himself and I still couldn't understand. I think he was probably using some kind of local slang.

"I'm sorry..." I started to say.

But before I could finish one of them pushed me into a tall hedge and they started kicking and punching me for no reason, screaming abuse at me as they did. I covered my head with my arms and tried to turn my body to shield myself but they kept pulling me around. I don't think I cried out. I was too scared and shocked, as I had been in the playground with Danny Keane; only this time there was no dinner lady to intervene. I have no idea how long the attack lasted; it probably wasn't more than thirty seconds. Everything was a blur, but I do have one clear impression of those moments: as I tried to protect myself with my arms I could see their faces, contorted into masks of pure hatred. I remember one of them particularly because he had an ugly scar running from the corner of his right eye down across his cheek.

At one point one of them shoved me roughly back into the hedge. In a kind of slow motion I felt myself sink into the privet, felt the branches give, then hold and support me before springing me outwards again. Using this impetus I pushed past their flailing fists and feet and ran blindly back up the hill to the row of shops where there was a fish and chip shop open. I don't know if they chased me, I didn't look back to see. Breathless with fear and the exertion of running I burst into the shop. Through the first tears I'd cried in a long, long time I blurted out what had happened. The chip shop owner went out to see if the boys were still there but they'd disappeared. He came back in and asked if I wanted to call my parents. I told him I was staying with my grandparents and that they didn't have a phone. I said I was scared to walk home on my own and he kindly offered to give me a lift. Leaving his wife in charge of the shop he put his arm around my shoulders and walked me back down to the hedge to get my school bag, which I'd dropped, before taking me to his car.

.....

I wouldn't see that scarred, hate-filled face again for twenty years but it stayed with me in my dreams. Many were the times through the rest of my teenage years - and beyond - when I woke in a sweat-soaked panic.

Despite my dislike of violence, I used to imagine smashing an iron bar or piece of timber into that face. Or, with cold surgical precision, carving a lattice of scalpel wounds across it.

Two decades later it didn't happen like that at all.

.....

The chip shop owner dropped me outside Grandma and Grandpa's house. I had described the boys to him on the journey and he said he had a good idea who they were if I wanted to report them, but I was too scared. He said if I changed my mind he would be happy to help in any way he could.

"If it's the lads I think it is they're nothing but trouble. They could do with getting their comeuppance," he added.

Grandma and Grandpa were sitting in front of the television when I walked in. My face was bruised and grazed, as were my arms, legs and a fair proportion of my body.

"God bless us and save us! What's happened?" exclaimed Grandma.

I was trying to control myself in front of them but as soon as I started to speak huge sobs took hold of me and I burst into tears again. I managed to tell them that I'd got lost on the way home and been beaten up by two big boys.

"What had you done do to make them set about you?" asked Grandpa when I'd calmed down a bit.

"Nothing. I don't know," I sniffled.

"Well, you must have done something," Grandma insisted unsympathetically.

"I hope you gave them a few digs yourself," said Grandpa, brightly. "'Give as good as you get', that's what my Da told me. 'They'll think twice about coming back again then'. He'd no time for cowards, my Da."

He'd obviously forgotten the way he let Big Mick talk to him. But worse than that he had put an idea into my head that hadn't occurred to me until then; that those boys might try to find me and beat me up again. I was terror-stricken as I realised they would have seen my school uniform so they'd know where to find me if they wanted to. "Come on up to the bathroom and let's get you cleaned up," said Grandma, a little more gently. "Make him a nice mug of sweet tea, will you, Grandpa."

And she took me upstairs to dab me with Dettol.

. . . . .

I have no doubt that Grandpa knew how to handle himself in a fight and probably had a few scraps in his time. And I can understand him backing down in the case of Big Mick, the 'man mountain'. But what he didn't seem to accept when I was beaten up, apart from the fact that I hated violence, was that there were two of these boys and they were both much bigger than me. When I pointed this out to him over the next few days he dismissed it as irrelevant.

"The bigger they are the harder they fall, Mason."

On one occasion he insisted on taking me out into the garden to show me how to throw a punch and do a bit of sparring.

"You've got to get your whole body into it, Mason. Make sure you follow right through with it. If you catch a fellow square on the button he'll not get back up again," he instructed me, coughing and wheezing after a quick show of fancy footwork. "Bit of bronchitis," he explained.

Despite his tough talk he wasn't the man he'd been seven years previous. He often got out of breath now and spent a lot more time in his favourite armchair watching television or reading the newspapers. Being the type of man he was he wouldn't bother the doctor unless it was something serious; and a bit of a cough and decline in vitality weren't worth the worry.

"He's not a young man any more," Grandma pointed out on more than one occasion. "And he should cut those cigarettes out."

It wasn't until he started coughing up blood a couple of years later that he decided it might be time to get a medical opinion. By that time it was too late and the cancer had spread from his lungs to his liver and other parts of his body. He didn't last long after that.

.....

After Danny Keane beat me up I had nightmares and I was wary of him at school but my day-to-day life wasn't affected beyond that.

After the second attack, fuelled by Grandpa's throwaway remark, my overactive imagination kept me on edge, turning me into a nervous wreck. The sound of footsteps behind me on the pavement was enough to set my heart pounding and force me to increase my pace while checking anxiously over my shoulder. Sudden noises had me flinching and jumping like a victim of shell shock. I developed a stooped, hunched posture, keeping my head down and avoiding eye contact with anyone on the street or in the playground at school. I never went out on my own at night and during the day the only places I went to - apart from the houses where I cleaned windows – were school, church, the local shops for Grandma and St. Angela's.

These self-imposed restrictions lasted until my mother returned and took me away again. It was one of the few things she ever did for which I was truly grateful.

11

During the seven months my mother was in the Middle East she wrote to us regularly but gave no hint there were any problems. Mind you, I don't suppose she would have told Grandma and Grandpa if things were going wrong; not because she wouldn't want to worry them, she just wouldn't want to give them a chance to say 'we told you so'.

I was never told the full story of why she came back from Saudi

Arabia but, from the snippets she let slip over the next three and a half years, I was able to piece together a reasonable account.

To start with she didn't like the job Andy had arranged for her; shut away in an office working as a secretary for a man she didn't get on with. She found it difficult coping with the restrictions that come with living in an Arab country. Then Andy was often away for days at a time visiting other sites for work. And she didn't really get on with the rest of the ex-pat community. All of which combined to leave her bored and frustrated. With only limited sources of entertainment available she soon drifted into old habits to keep herself amused; in such a small community it didn't take long for the gossip and rumours to get back to Andy. When he told her he didn't want anything more to do with her at about the same time as her boss decided he'd had enough of her as well, there was nothing to keep her there.

.....

Within weeks of us moving back into the maisonette my mother received a letter from the council informing her that the tenement was being pulled down and we were going to be re-housed. We were both quite happy about this.

Because she wasn't too fussy about relocation we were moved almost immediately to a fairly new house on the other side of town. This meant another, final change of school for me; and not just a change of school but a change of denomination too. For the first time ever I went to a Church of England school, Rookwood Comprehensive, which we chose on the simple basis that it was the nearest to our new house.

.....

Almost as soon as we left Grandma and Grandpa's I had told my mother that I didn't want to go to mass anymore. I expected an argument and had a whole list of reasons prepared but she replied, quite evenly:

"OK. If you don't want to go you don't have to."

And that was that. I was quite shocked by her indifference. I don't know if it's because she thought I was old enough to make up my own mind about religion; or whether she just couldn't be bothered to argue; or what? I wondered if she had lost her own faith – assuming she ever really had any – and broached the subject a few months later, asking her if she still believed in God.

"I don't know," she answered.

"Why do you bother going to church, then? If you don't know?" I pressed her.

"Habit I suppose. Anyway, it does no harm does it?" she replied.

I think that was probably the deepest theological or philosophical discussion I ever had with my mother.

.....

The council house came with a small garden; the first we had had since leaving Manning Road. It was overgrown when we moved in but, undeterred by my lack of horticultural know-how, I set about turning it into something resembling Dadda's.

The previous tenants had left one or two rusty tools propped up against the coalbunker and what I lacked I borrowed from neighbours. In the case of the lawn mower, when I eventually got around to needing it, I had an arrangement with Mrs. Collyer, an old lady living three doors down; she lent me her mower in return for me cutting her grass.

'Fair exchange is no robbery', as Grandma would have said.

The first few sessions were solid graft, clearing the tangle of weeds that stood waist high in some places. Once that was done I dug it over, picking out unwanted roots and weeds and sieving the earth to achieve a fine, clean topsoil. The next thing was trying to convince my mother to get some turf to lay; usually she wasn't too keen spending money on anything other than essentials like food, bills, rent, cigarettes and gin. I was wondering what I could do to persuade her when I came home one afternoon to find a pile of turf rolls heaped up against our front wall.

"Where did these come from?" I asked her when she arrived home.

"I met a chap last night who works for the corporation," she explained. "He pulled a few strings with the parks department."

"How much did it cost?" I asked.

"Nothing," she replied airily, lighting a cigarette.

'You don't get anything for nothing in this life' was another of Grandma's sayings but I didn't question my mother any further.

By the time the cold weather arrived the lawn was established. With the aid of a couple of gardening books borrowed from the library, a small cash injection from my mother and a bit of pilfering from a local park, I had installed a few hardy shrubs and planted some bulbs for the spring.

Three and a half years later, just before I left the house and my mother once and for all, the garden was an attractive well-ordered homage to the back of number 163 Manning Road.

·····

It was a pleasant surprise to find that Mr. Flowers had moved to Rookwood where he'd taken up the post of Head of English. He, in turn, was happy to see the continued improvement in my written English. He carried on his practice of lending me books and we sometimes met for coffee outside school to discuss them. He also took time to discuss problems I was having with other subjects at school, offering advice and encouragement, particularly when it came down to revising for exams.

It was while I was at Rookwood that I also made my first real friends since I'd shouted 'Merry Christmas' and 'See you next year' to Simon Stanley and David Shepherd outside St. Mike's.

Actually, in Patrick's case he was more a kindred spirit than just a friend.

Patrick Russell, a hulking lumpen lank-haired youth, was two years above me at Rookwood; I was in the fourth year, he was in the lower sixth. Usually there wasn't much social interaction between the different years but we got to know each other outside school.

The local cemetery, Carsons Green, was a huge sprawling place with a crematorium and multi-denominational chapel. There rarely seemed to be more than a handful of people around at any one time and I used to feel safer there than anywhere else outside our new house. One Saturday afternoon, about halfway through the autumn term, I slipped into the back of the chapel during a funeral service. It was a low-key affair and the place was almost empty, so I couldn't help but notice Patrick sitting opposite me on the other side of the central aisle. As we filed out behind the coffin and a small group of mourners Patrick nodded to me.

"Relative of yours?" he asked.

"No."

"Friend?"

"No. Yours?"

"No. You're that new kid aren't you?"

"Yes."

"Thought I recognised you. So what are you doing here?"

"I don't know. I just like it here. It's peaceful," I floundered, self-consciously.

"Yeah, I know what you mean," he agreed.

"What about you?"

"I have a morbid curiosity about death," he announced in a significant, rather dramatic way.

"Oh, I see," I replied lamely.

And that was the beginning of our friendship, which stayed firm until I moved away.

Patrick liked to get more involved in the whole thing than I did. For instance, he dressed in black, a style he introduced into his school uniform in his final year and which I sometimes copied outside school. He was also quite happy to mingle with the mourners at the graveside if there were sufficient numbers for him to go unnoticed. And he'd take service cards and join in with the prayers and hymns, something I'd never do.

It was Patrick who got me interested in music: atmospheric progressive rock of the early to mid-Seventies that we'd listen to lying on the floor of his darkened bedroom. There were a lot of instrumental tracks with elaborate keyboard and guitar solos and some of the earliest synthesizers; and songs with fantastical lyrics that must have drawn on the types of stories I enjoyed reading so much.

The only other contemporary music I really got into was some of the darker material of the late Seventies and early Eighties; bands like

Joy Division and Bauhaus, David Bowie's Berlin period, that sort of stuff. These days I tend to listen to classical music. I'm no connoisseur - and my little radio/cassette player doesn't give me particularly good sound quality - but I like to have it on quietly in the background when I'm reading or dropping off to sleep.

Patrick was also heavily into horror and witchcraft. His favourite author was Edgar Allen Poe and, before I knew him, he had managed to get in, under age, to see *The Exorcist*, the most terrifying and controversial film of its time. His bedroom was decorated in black emulsion with a huge silver pentacle expertly painted on the ceiling and was always lit by banks of candles. (He claimed he never turned on the electric light.) He was convinced there was a coven of devil worshippers operating in the area and he used to make regular nocturnal visits to Carsons Green in the hope of catching them desecrating graves or performing satanic rituals.

"I know they're around here somewhere," he told me on more than one occasion. "I've seen the signs."

He never told me what the signs were, though. And, to the best of my knowledge, he never found the coven. I'm not sure what his intentions were if he had discovered anything; whether he just wanted to watch or join in.

Despite his morbid interest in death and fascination with all things supernatural and sinister Patrick was a pleasant, down-to-earth lad. His parents were nice people who indulged his whims with good humour and his sister Katherine, who was a year younger than him, was an attractive, popular girl. I know a lot of people thought he was a bit weird – and possibly thought I was too – but I was very glad I bumped into him at Carsons Green that autumn day because I spent a lot of time with him over the next three years.

.....

There was a definite shift in the terms of my relationship with my mother during that first term. What with her readiness to accept my decision to stop going to church, the surprise of the photography book she gave me for my birthday and then her help in getting the turf for the lawn, I almost started liking her.

During those three months, while I was enduring the usual settling-in period at the new school and she was trying to find a new job and make new friends, there seemed to be a closing of ranks. I think she started to regard me as an equal and she certainly approved when I got a part-time job, stacking shelves and sweeping up in a local grocery shop. Whether this was appreciation of my initiative and endeavour per se or more to do with the fact that she no longer felt obliged to give me pocket money, I'm not sure. However, when I expressed an interest in music she made a donation towards a second-hand hi-fi and even gave me half towards my first album, Pink Floyd's *Wish You Were Here*.

But by Christmas of that year Brenda had moved in next door with her bellowing, rasping voice, her foul language and a boyfriend who she had kicked out by New Year's Eve. Her arrival saw an end to that brief period when there had seemed to be the possibility of a real relationship developing between my mother and me. Instead they became best friends – horrible together, sharing a seemingly insatiable appetite for alcohol, cigarettes and men - while my mother and I became strangers again; living separate lives, communicating only out of necessity and, as time went on, in increasingly bitter tones.

12

With Mr. Flowers' help and encouragement I surprised a lot people, myself included, by passing five 'O' levels: English Language, English Literature, Woodwork, History and, ironically, Religious Studies. Even more amazingly I got a grade one CSE - the equivalent of an 'O' level pass - in Maths.

I never really got to grips with maths and the sciences. I found it difficult understanding abstract theories or remembering tables and equations. The maths grade I got was the result of lucky guessing in the multiple-choice sections, a grasp of basic arithmetic and an interest in geometry, which almost certainly developed out of its practical applications in woodwork. Algebra was a complete mystery to me and so remains to this day.

I hadn't really considered staying on at school after the fifth form. Before I got my results I thought I'd probably try to get an apprenticeship as a carpenter and study for a City and Guilds qualification. It was Mr. Flowers who suggested I carry on into the sixth form to take English Literature and History 'A' levels and try for an 'O' Level in technical drawing. He thought the latter might be useful if I did decide to move into carpentry or the building trade. He showed tremendous faith in me and gave me constant support throughout the time I knew him. I know he must have been saddened and disappointed when I disappeared from school. One of the greatest regrets of my life is that I never said 'goodbye' or 'thank you' to him.

.....

At the start of the sixth form a new kid came to Rookwood and joined our class. Howie Hinckley was small, quiet, intense and intelligent. He would have been accepted at the local grammar school but his father was a raving socialist who didn't want any son of his going to a Trust school.

"If a state education was good enough for me, son, it's good enough for you," he told Howie. Mind you, considering he ended up departmental foreman in a plastics factory I doubt he ever had the same academic promise as his son.

Not long after Howie started we discovered we shared an interest in science fiction, fantasy and 'sword and sorcery'. We soon started a brisk trade swapping our favourite titles and authors and hung around together at break-times. Back then I used to own quite a few books as that was all I spent my money on, apart from records.

Patrick was doing an art foundation course by this time. When I introduced him to Howie they immediately hit it off as they were both into heavy metal and the paranormal so, once again, I found myself one third of a little clique; the first time I'd felt part of a gang or group since leaving St. Mike's. The three of us spent a lot of time together, often meeting in town to scour the record stores and cult bookshops in search of rare items and bargains. We must have been an amusing sight: one big and bulky, one miniaturised and one like a beanpole, all dressed in sober black; like a clutch of refugees from 'The Addams Family'.

.....

On Saturdays I only had to work mornings at the grocery shop, so in the afternoons I'd sometimes go with Patrick to a funeral at Carsons Green. Howie came with us a couple of times but it wasn't his cup of tea; he couldn't understand why we'd want to watch a load of strangers crying over another, dead stranger. Then, sometime during my first term in the lower sixth, much to Patrick's disgust, I lost interest in going to funerals too. I'm not quite sure why. Maybe I just had better things to do.

I still enjoyed my own company – and there were times when I went out of my way to be on my own – but usually I was happiest spending time with Patrick or Howie or the pair of them together. Without realising it I was growing and developing as a social being. Going to school and trips into town became pleasant experiences. I looked forward to things. I began to have a life. I was starting to become someone.

.....

Halfway through my first term in the lower sixth Grandpa died. He'd been diagnosed with cancer at the start of the summer and his prognosis hadn't been good. Grandma, who had the phone connected by this time, rang my mother on a regular basis urging her to go and visit him before it was too late. Over the next couple of months my mother kept putting it off, making excuse after weak excuse, usually saying she couldn't afford it despite having enough money to spend on regular nights out with Brenda. Eventually Grandma sent the coach fare for the two of us, followed by yet another phone call to say that Grandpa was fading fast and we might not have another chance to see him alive. Still my mother delayed until the call came from her brother to say that Grandpa had passed away and asking, cynically, whether she was thinking of turning up for the funeral.

Having been to so many funerals for people I didn't know I wondered if it would be any different attending one for someone I did. As it turned out, apart from feeling a bit sorry for Grandma who wept throughout, I was as detached at Grandpa's as I had been at any of the others. And by all outward appearances my mother was equally unmoved. While her sisters, nieces and nephews wept – and even her brother looked a little watery about the eyes – she remained stony-faced throughout the service in St. Mike's and looked positively bored at the graveside.

Our lack of emotion didn't go unnoticed. At the reception in Grandma's house I overheard people talking about me; comments such as 'his mother's son' and 'just the same as her'. I felt like telling them they knew nothing about me and that I was nothing like my mother, but I kept my mouth shut; I didn't want to give them more cause for comparison.

Meanwhile she was getting the third degree about why she hadn't made it to see Grandpa before he'd died. She started by saying she couldn't afford it with only one income coming into the house but when she realised this wasn't going to wash she changed tack.

"I kept hearing from Mum how Dad was wasting away. How much pain he was in. I didn't want to see him like that," she croaked, dragging on her cigarette shakily and allowing a tear to escape the corner of her eye. "I wanted to remember him like he was, not lying in a hospital bed being eaten away by cancer."

Her time watching matinee idols had obviously not been wasted. I doubt that everyone was taken in by her performance but it took some of the pressure off her.

I spent most of that afternoon sitting under the shelves in the front room, observing these people who were my flesh and blood, wishing I could be almost anywhere else in the world. I didn't really know any of them and I had no desire to get to know them. It was made fairly clear by everyone there, with the exception of Grandma, that the feeling was mutual.

.....

I can't remember for sure but, now I think of it, it might have been after Grandpa's funeral that I stopped going to funerals at Carsons Green. Possibly because I saw for the first time all of the petty family politics and hypocrisy behind the united front of grief that's on display in church and at the cemetery.

.....

Back in our council house the following night I heard my mother, drunk in the company of Brenda, launch into a vicious verbal attack on her own family; making snide comments and bitchy criticisms, exposing long-held family secrets and making all kinds of unpleasant insinuations. Fuelled with gin she went on for ages while I lay on my bed with a pillow pulled over my ears, trying not to listen but unable to avoid snatches of her ranting as she stamped and raged downstairs.

It wasn't long after this that she started telling me the truth about my grandparents and the part they had played in cutting me off from Dadda.

.....

Within six months of Grandpa's funeral Grandma seemed to have forgotten his great ideal of family unity that she'd supported so staunchly while he was alive. Despite having two daughters, a son and several grandchildren living near her - several of whom, it transpired at the funeral, had marriage problems, financial difficulties and job worries - she sold the house on Manning Road and took the proceeds and her not inconsiderable savings back to Ireland where she moved in with her sister.

The last time I saw her was the day after the funeral as my mother and I were leaving.

"You haven't got that money I sent for the coach, have you?" she asked my mother. "Your father's funeral's crippled me."

My mother said she'd send it to her. I have no idea whether she did or not.

Then Grandma turned to me.

"Goodbye Mason, love. I hope you find happiness. God knows

you're not the child you were and that's a sad thing."

I don't know if the tear she sniffed back was for me or for herself.

13

I'm sure part of my reluctance to start drinking before I was eighteen came from seeing how obnoxiously my mother and her friends behaved when they were drunk. As I had spent most of the time from the age of seven trying to stay in control of myself I was loath to let that control slip.

I enjoy my drink now and, while it's likely I would have started drinking at some time in my life anyway, I'm glad the habit is a legacy of my friendship with Patrick and Howie. Every now and then I remember that fact and raise a glass, or a can, to their memory and drink to their health and happiness.

.....

I was never interested in taking photographs of people so I have no pictures of Patrick and Howie, or my mother or grandparents. In one of my albums I've kept three photos of the many I took in Carsons Green cemetery. Two are close-ups of gravestones, focusing on the composition of textures created by weathering and decay and the patterns of lichen, grasses and ivy covering the stones. The other was taken on the last New Year's Day I spent in my mother's house.

I rose early, before seven, not long after the last of my mother's guests had left. As I made my way through the cold silent dark of the winter's morning the world seemed deserted, like that Christmas morning with Dadda. With no snow to muffle my footsteps they echoed metallically off the houses of the terraced streets.

I entered Carsons Green through a broken section of the perimeter wall. A small brook ran along the edge of the east side of the cemetery – its oldest section - and from it a thickening mist was creeping across the graves and pathways, wrapping itself around shrubs, bushes and trees. I headed to a favourite spot in a small hollow near the stream and waited for the sun to rise. It was a long wait and, despite sipping tea from the flask I had with me, I was damp and shivering by the time I noticed a gradual brightening in the sky. The mist had continued to drift over the cemetery and I didn't see the pale, ghostly circle of the sun until it was clear of the horizon, seemingly entangled in the branches of the silhouetted trees.

I took several pictures that morning but the one I kept was the one that best caught the atmosphere and ethereal beauty of the moment. The brook, the pallid disc of the sun barely visible through the curling mist, the glint of thin light on dew drops and spiders webs, several awkwardly leaning gravestones and a mausoleum, all caught in a frame of ghostly elms. It remains one of my favourite pictures, taken by anyone.

I have several other photos from that time, either nature shots or unusual perspectives of manmade objects – and a couple of snaps of my feet, of course – but none of people. I now have seven albums containing mainly black-and-white photographs. In all seven albums there are possibly ten or a dozen pictures with people in them and, in every case, those people are incidental strangers.

It's not often I look at the albums these days. When I do it's to enjoy the pictures for their aesthetic value rather than for any memory connected with them. Every now and then I'll decide I don't like a certain picture any more and I'll throw it out so that, here and there, there are gaps within the pages. In fact, there are probably enough gaps to make up a whole album now. Maybe I should rearrange them and create that album; a book full of blanks. It would still be representative of my life. Possibly more so than the pictures.

. . . . .

When I told the first woman I had sex with that she'd taken my virginity she wanted me to take her picture.

"What for?" I asked.

"So you can remember me. So you can remember the first woman with who you make love," she said in her charming French accent.

Not wanting to offend her I snapped away at her several times as she draped herself across her bed, pouting provocatively or smiling coyly. She wasn't to know there was no film in the camera.

…..

Within a period of approximately two weeks either side of my eighteenth birthday several things happened that, cumulatively, helped make my decision to leave my mother.

The first was the occasion when I realised I didn't have to walk the streets in constant fear of being attacked. Of being a victim. I remember the moment with crystal clarity.

I was in town one Saturday afternoon, on my way to meet Howie in a favourite coffee shop. As usual when I was alone I was avoiding making eye contact with anyone, keeping my focus on the pavement a few feet ahead, when I bumped into someone in the crowd. Before I had a chance to make my excuses he spoke first:

"Oh! I'm sorry," he muttered.

"No, no. It's my fault," I replied, glancing up at him.

He was probably in his mid-twenties and, while slightly shorter than me, was solidly built. Not unlike Corbin in fact.

"No, really, it's my fault. I'm very sorry," he apologised again.

And as I looked into his face I was sure I saw anxiety in his eyes. When I hauled Corbin to the back of the classroom a couple of years earlier his expression had been a mixture of shock and disbelief; but not fear, I don't think. There in the street I was looking into the face of someone who was afraid of me. He was scared of me.

"That's OK," I said and watched him slink away.

Carrying on towards the coffee shop I experimented, tentatively, catching people's eyes and holding their gaze for a second. Then two seconds. Then three. Some people stared back but that was the worst that happened. Most people actually looked away. They weren't all waiting for an excuse to pick a fight with me or beat me up. I was just another face in the crowd, attracting more or less the same amount of attention as anyone else.

From that day on I stopped being quite so afraid of the rest of the human race; of footsteps behind me; of sudden noises and my own

125

shadow. The change didn't happen in that instant, it was a gradual process, but I slowly learned to move through life with more confidence, which eventually manifested itself as a kind of aloofness. I erected an invisible barrier around myself and, in so doing, I unwittingly copied something I'd seen over a decade before on Manning Road.

.....

The second thing that happened was my eighteenth birthday itself. Coming of age. Legally I was an adult and able to make my own decisions.

Not that that would have made a difference if my mother had pushed me to the point she did before I was eighteen; I would have left anyway. But being eighteen made it easier because I knew she had no power to come after me, or challenge anything I did.

.....

And the third thing was Brenda assaulting me on the night of my birthday, which was the catalyst for the final chain of events that led to my departure.

I was used to my mother making fun of me in front of her friends when she was drunk. I had learned to ignore her. And them. But allowing Brenda to foist herself on me sexually upset and angered me, especially as I lay in bed that night listening to them squawking about it downstairs, like a couple of old hags. I tried to forget about it until one evening, about a week later, when my mother came home after being in the pub for a couple of hours. She started teasing me and asking what was wrong with me: wasn't I interested in women? Or sex? It wasn't because I was more interested in boys was it? And what did I get up to with my two 'geeky friends' when she was out of the house anyway?

I don't know why this got under my skin so much when I had put up with all her other taunts and insults over the years, but it did. And, of course, I was still incensed about the incident with Brenda.

It wasn't unusual for me to answer my mother back but usually

I did it in a flippant, offhand manner, making my point without rousing her anger. But this time I didn't hold back, I let it all come out.

"Is it any wonder I've got no interest in sex when I've had to listen to you grunting and groaning and banging away with a procession of drunks every night? Like an animal! Is that supposed to make me interested in sex? Because it hasn't! If anything it's put me right off!"

She sat at the kitchen table, stunned into silence for once. I left her there and went into the garden where I calmed down, taking deep breaths and pretending to busy myself with some weeding. After a few minutes I noticed her standing at the living room window, watching me through the net curtain. I ignored her and a few seconds later heard the slamming of the front door. From that moment everything snowballed out of control.

I didn't see her for a couple of days. She avoided me purposely, staying out late and going straight to bed when she came in, then leaving the house without breakfast early in the mornings. When I came home from work the following Saturday afternoon there was still no sign of her. I had lunch and tidied the kitchen. Then, as we were in the middle of a bit of a heat wave, I thought I'd better water the lawn and flowerbeds.

Of all the mean, vengeful things she'd done over the years nothing compared with the malicious destruction she had wreaked on the garden. The shrubs and flowers had been ripped up and trampled, she had dug great holes in the lawn, she had smashed the window box and potted plants against the coalbunker and she had broken or mangled whatever tools she was able to. I was stunned.

Once I'd taken in the full extent of the devastation I ran up to my room to see what damage she'd done there, but she had confined her violence to the garden. I don't know if she was drunk when she wrecked everything but, to be honest, it doesn't matter; I'm fairly sure it was premeditated. For two days she had all that bile and anger festering inside her, gnawing away while she tried to come up with the most hurtful, effective way of exacting her revenge. The garden was my place; I had created it and I looked after it. She knew exactly what she was doing when she tore it to pieces and in doing so she showed how low she was capable of sinking. And she hadn't finished yet.

.....

During the years we spent in the council house there had indeed been a procession of men spending the night with my mother. In that time she only had one relationship of any consequence, with a builder called Paul. He worked away from home most of the time, coming back at weekends, which gave my mother ample opportunity to have other lovers if she felt so inclined. Which she often did.

Paul's demise was the usual scenario: he wanted some level of commitment, my mother wouldn't give it; he said without some guarantee he would walk away, she said "Fine"; he walked away, she couldn't have cared less.

The walls of the council house were thin – as were the walls of the other places we had lived in – so if I was awake when my mother had company it was impossible not to hear them. I think there is something horribly sordid about listening to people having sex. Even when you try to block out the sounds of the squeaking bedsprings, the headboard rattling against the wall, the whole range of grunts, gasps and groans, it is almost impossible to avoid conjuring up images of what is happening: heaving sweaty bodies and contorted, grimacing faces. And when it's your own mother it's even more unpleasant.

It would be easy to say that my mother just enjoyed sex. Maybe she did. However, when she was younger she had always used sex, or the promise of it, to get something she wanted. But when she gave herself to those men in those last couple of years, what did she get in return then? Who was using whom? Maybe the company of a man, even if it was just for one night of drunken passion, helped her convince herself that she wasn't lonely. Maybe that was all she wanted.

.....

It would have been easy to respond to my mother's destruction of the garden by trashing something of hers, but I resisted the temptation. I didn't want to lower myself to her level and I didn't want a war. Instead I took the course of action that I knew would irritate her most: I cut back the shrubs and flowers, salvaging what I could; I swept up the broken earthenware and soil; I replaced clumps of turf and tidied up generally. And then I acted as though nothing had happened.

My mother loved winding people up to get a reaction out of them; to goad them into an argument. I wasn't going to give her that satisfaction.

When she arrived home later that afternoon I had cooked dinner for the two of us, leaving hers on a plate in the oven.

"What's this?" she asked. "Poison?"

"No. Why?" I replied innocently.

"What do you mean, 'Why?'" she sneered.

"It's your dinner. If you don't want it I'll eat it later," I told her. "I'm going out for a bit. See you."

And I breezed out of the house, breathing a sigh of relief.

I didn't see her when I got home that evening; nor on Sunday morning. After breakfast I went out and spent the day with Patrick, listening to music and melting candles, moulding the wax into different shapes. When I told him about the garden he suggested we make an effigy of my mother and stick pins in it, but I told him not to bother; mainly because I didn't believe in voodoo and black magic. We had a good laugh though and it was a quiet, relaxing day that took my mind off things at home. Unfortunately it turned out to be the calm before the storm.

When I got home that evening my mother was in the kitchen with Brenda, who started on me as soon as I walked through the door.

"Hello Macey-boy," she slurred. "Where've you been?"

"At a friend's," I answered politely.

"How's your garden?" she asked with a snort, blowing cigarette smoke out her nostrils and reinforcing the 'old dragon' image I had of her.

I should have let it go but I made the mistake of answering

129

her again.

"Why do you ask?"

"I hear there's been a bit of vandalism done on it."

"Nothing that can't be fixed," I told her.

"You're not all upset then?" she asked, speaking in a coo-ey baby voice.

"It's nothing that can't be fixed," I repeated.

"You're very calm about it, aren't you? I'd be livid."

"Yes, well, I'm not you," I pointed out.

My mother had been silent up to this point. Her pinhole eyes and lack of co-ordination in getting her glass of gin to her lips betrayed her degree of drunkenness.

"It's no good, Bren. You won't get him going. He's just like his old Dadda," she drawled.

"How's that then? You told me he wasn't his real father, didn't you?" Brenda asked.

"Yes, but I don't know...," my mother replied. "Something went wrong somewhere. He's turned out just like him. Another half-a-man."

In the eleven years after we left Manning Road my mother rarely spoke about Dadda. When she did she sometimes adopted a slightly derogatory tone, but she was never blatantly rude about him or questioned his decency as a human being; or his manhood.

"Oh, he wasn't another one was he?" Brenda asked.

I could feel my hackles start to rise. It was bad enough my mother casting aspersions on my friends but I wasn't going to stand there and listen to her and Brenda bad-mouthing Dadda.

"Another what?" I challenged her.

"Well, I don't know, Macey-boy. What are you?" Brenda asked.

"I don't know what you're going on about but don't you talk about my Dadda," I hissed, pointing my finger at her. "You never knew him, so shut up!"

"Ooh, I think we've hit a nerve there," she crowed.

"Dadda was a good man. Better than any of the idiots she's hitched herself up with since!"

"He was perfect, wasn't he Mason?" My mother drew herself up, rocking and swaying on the kitchen chair. "Above criticism, wasn't he? Your precious Dadda? Well let me tell you some things about your Dadda. He was a sad, boring, stupid man who people laughed at behind his back. And I'll tell you something else. He was a pervert! A peeping Tom."

"You're a liar!" I snapped.

"I'm not. It's true. I used to leave my bedroom door open at night to get a breeze through when it was hot. And he'd creep onto the landing at the top of the stairs and watch me getting undressed through the crack in the door. He thought I didn't know he was there but I did."

"You're lying!"

"No I'm not. He was a dirty old man."

"You are! You're lying! Why didn't you shut the door if you knew he was there?"

"It didn't bother me. I had a good body; nothing to be ashamed of. Give the sad old perv a thrill."

"Maybe Macey's turned out like him," Brenda sneered. "Maybe he likes to watch. One of them voyeurs."

"I know he likes to listen," my mother added, viciously. "Don't you, Mason?"

"No!?" Brenda affected mock surprise. My mother had obviously told her what I'd said a few days earlier. "He doesn't, does he? You little pervert! I bet he tells his little bum-boy friends about it too, don't you Macey?"

I stood in silence while they mocked me. I couldn't believe anyone could be so cruel and vile. And, in my mother's case, to her own son! I watched them guzzling gin and sucking on their cigarettes, hollowing their already-sunken cheeks; if Patrick wanted to find witches he was looking in the wrong place.

"Dirty little devil! Listening to your own mother!" Brenda rasped again.

But I didn't care any more; my decision was made.

"Don't worry," I told them. "I'll never listen to her again."

And I grabbed a coat and walked out.

.....

131

Dadda was a good man, 'a living saint' as my grandmother described him, so I find it hard to believe my mother's story about him spying on her. I'm not saying it couldn't have happened because, after all, he was just a man who must have had urges, but it's more likely that she made the whole thing up to get at me. Having attacked me, my friends and then my garden she knew the only thing left that was precious to me was Dadda, so she tried to defile his memory.

I don't know whether her telling that story was another premeditated act or if it happened in the heat of the moment, but either way it was the final nail in the coffin.

.....

When I walked out of the door I knew it was over. What I didn't know was what I was going to do next. I went to Carson's Green where I wandered amongst the tombstones in the warm night air, trying to clear my head and figure out a plan of action.

Patrick had been talking about getting a flat sometime but I couldn't stand to wait indefinitely; I wanted to get out of my mother's house immediately. I'd have to find somewhere else to live if I wanted to finish school. Then, for the first time since I decided to stay on into the sixth form, I thought seriously about my long-term future. Even assuming I passed my 'A' levels, which was by no means certain, would they be of any use to me? I still didn't know what job I wanted to do. Anyway, the most important thing now was getting away from my mother. Even though I'd calmed down by this time I was still sickened by her and, in the end, the decision was relatively easy to make: I'd get away completely. The hardest part was going to be leaving my friends behind.

The next decision to make was where to go. As I had no friends or ties anywhere I tried to think of places that held some significance for me. Inevitably, Australia sprang to mind. I fantasised for a while about tracking down Dadda but I knew this was an impossible dream. Apart from anything else I didn't have the kind of money for a trip like that. However, the idea of going abroad had been put into my head and, mainly because I had learned a few words of French,

I decided to go to France.

Lying in my favourite hollow in the cemetery in the early hours of the morning, wrapped in my coat, I worked through the details of my plan. I listed the things I would need to take: birth certificate so I could get a passport; post office savings book; minimum necessary clothing. And I listed the things I wanted to take: my two carvings; my cameras; my photography book and my albums.

As the birds started singing and the rabbits hopped out of their burrows to graze I dozed off for an hour or so, my body a little cold and stiff but my mind settled. When I woke I went to see Patrick before he left for college. He didn't try to talk me out of running away. If anything he encouraged me.

"If that's what you've got to do then that's what you've got to do," he said solemnly, paraphrasing the old cowboy philosophy.

He lent me his rucksack and an old one-man tent – neither of which he got back; although I doubt he ever thought he would – and promised he'd say 'Goodbye' to Howie for me.

"Send me a postcard," he called as I closed his garden gate.

"I will," I told him. But I never did.

I let myself quietly into my mother's house and, once I was sure she was out, I found my birth certificate and savings book, packed the rucksack and made a pile of sandwiches for the journey.

Sitting at the kitchen table eating a hearty cooked breakfast I flicked through an old road atlas Paul had left behind, working out the quickest route to Dover. I had decided to hitchhike rather than spend money on a train or coach ticket and I didn't want to waste any time. Now that my mind was made up I was keen to get on with it before I had second thoughts.

As I was nodding off in the cemetery that morning I'd been trying to think of some grand gesture I could make, some statement of defiance and disgust that my mother would find when she got home. But as I washed up my breakfast things and wiped the table clean I realised there was no need. What I was doing should make the point eloquently enough.

I put the road atlas back into the cupboard under the sink and checked around to make sure I'd left everything tidy. Then I hoisted the rucksack onto my shoulders, dropped my house keys into a junk drawer in one of the kitchen units, walked out of the front door and closed it behind me.

PART FOUR

1

Two days later I found myself in Calais, where I stayed for just over a week. For most travellers from Britain Calais is a point of arrival onto mainland Europe; a starting place for their trips. While I was there I watched them turn up at the campsite in the afternoons or evenings. They'd pitch their tents, cook a meal on their Calor Gas stoves, drink some cheap French wine, go to bed and be gone before I got up the next morning.

For me Calais was a starting point as well but I needed more time to come to terms with what I had done and to gather my courage; which, initially at least, was of the Dutch variety. I had cut myself off from everything and everyone I knew and, despite many years spent in my own company, I felt lonely and scared. So, having had my first real drink only a few days earlier, I landed in France and turned to alcohol to help dull those feelings. It took some time to develop a tolerance, and I had quite a few rough nights and hung-over mornings in the first couple of months, but I soon learned to enjoy the fruits of the vine and the hop pole.

.....

I remember vividly my first night in Calais: the lights from the ferry terminal threw the outline of the surrounding sand dunes into relief and a couple of stars shone in the deepening blue sky. As I sat outside my poorly erected tent in the gathering dusk, eating plain baguette and swigging cheap French beer out of litre bottles, a tall slim African guy wandered onto the campsite. He had peppercorn hair, no shoes on his feet, wore jeans and a waistcoat but no shirt, had a smallish pack over one shoulder and a guitar slung over the other. He ambled about, carefully inspecting the ground, testing it with his feet in search of a good pitch. There was something magnetic about him and I noticed I wasn't the only one who was

135

following his progress. Eventually he found a spot to his liking, unrolled his carry mat, sat down and started strumming his guitar. Within half an hour he had a crowd around him, someone had lit a small fire and the group of ten or twelve strangers were preparing a communal meal. They shared food and drink and sang songs while I sat just outside the glow of their fire, partaking without joining in.

As I drank myself into a stupor I wondered what it must have been like to be him.

.....

I spent eight or nine days in Calais before waking one morning and deciding it was time to move on. I packed up, got onto the road, stuck out my thumb and was soon picked up by a car heading east.

During that first trip abroad I learned how to survive on a shoe-string budget, adapting to a lifestyle of foraging, stealing (when absolutely necessary), sleeping rough and improvising. I also picked up a few basic phrases in French and, over the years, learned to speak some elementary German, Italian and Spanish as well, but I never went beyond the fundamentals. This was partly laziness but also because I was quite happy to remain incommunicado.

.....

On the evening of my nineteenth birthday I found myself on the west coast of France, somewhere on the Bay of Biscay. As I wandered along the shore, with a bottle of cheap white wine in each hand, I spotted a piece of bleached driftwood near the dunes on the landward edge of the beach and I made a detour to pick it up. Sitting on a craggy outcrop a few minutes later, swigging wine and absentmindedly hitting the stick off the rocks, I watched a couple of sailboats cutting across the bay in the warm, stiff breeze. I was considering hurling the stick out beyond the headland to see how long it would take for the waves to wash it ashore again – a kind of one-man, tidal version of 'Pooh Sticks'; but as I weighed it in my hand I saw something in it that made me think of Stan, the old gravedigger at St. Angela's. I probably hadn't thought about Stan since I last saw him at Grandpa's funeral, leaning against an ivy-covered wall smoking a cigarette while he waited to fill in the grave.

I had a small shoulder bag with me in which I always carried a few important and useful items such as my passport, travellers' cheques, camera, a hat, a torch, a Swiss army knife and a larger, sturdier, rustic lock knife, which I now took out and opened. Chipping away at the stick, shaping it, I tried to get the curve of Stan's bent back, his hunched shoulders, the jut of his chin, the strange trapezoid shape of his head and the flatness of his features. After a while a combination of diminishing light and diminishing hand-eye co-ordination forced me to stop but I hung onto the piece of wood and finished the job the next day. The carving I ended up with probably looked nothing like Stan but it did look like an old man and I think it was a decent first attempt.

Considering the associations woodcarving had with Dadda it's strange that I had never tried it before; but after that first effort on the Bay of Biscay I often passed the time whittling, a hobby I have pursued intermittently to the present day.

.....

The last time I saw the paper knife I made at St. Paul's it was imbedded in the upholstery of Danny's hanging chair, left there by my mother when she'd tried to stab him with it after he slapped her. I suppose it stayed in his flat when we moved out. I have no idea what happened to all the other things I made in school woodwork classes; hopefully some of them found good homes somewhere.

.....

A month after my twentieth birthday, as autumn was edging towards winter, I was heading from Spain through southern France on my way back to England. I had been given a lift by a guy who was so drunk he kept dozing off at the wheel, only to start awake and accelerate madly until we were bumper to bumper with the car in front, at which point he would brake, decelerate and doze off again. And so it went on. It was a scary ride and I was glad to get out of the car; that is until I realised he had left me, just as night was falling, at a tiny junction on an unlit road in the middle of nowhere. Not exactly perfect conditions for hitching. I didn't hold out much hope of getting a lift that evening and I resigned myself to sleeping under a hedge in a roadside ditch, so it was a pleasant surprise when a car pulled over after only a few minutes. I ran up and stuck my head in the window. The driver was a young woman who said something in French that I didn't understand.

"Pardon. Je suis Anglais. Je ne parle pas français," I told her. "Allez vers le Nord?"

"Yes. I am going to the north," she answered, smiling.

"It's OK?" I asked.

It was unusual to get a lift from a solitary woman, even more so at night, so I thought I'd give her the opportunity to opt out if she wasn't sure of me.

"Yes. Please, it's OK," she said, leaning across to open the door and signalling me to get in.

I dumped my pack in the back and climbed into the passenger seat. As we pulled away she asked where I was going and I explained I was heading for Calais.

"It is a long way," she pointed out.

"Yes, I know," I replied. "How far are you going?"

"One hundred kilometres. A small town. Where you will stay tonight?"

"I don't know. Is there a campsite in your town?"

"I don't think."

"It doesn't matter, I'll find somewhere. It's a nice night," I said, pointing at the moon that was brightening the sky ahead of us.

She laughed and we drove on for a while in silence until she introduced herself, telling me her name was Celestine. Then she asked about my travels. Her English was pretty good and she seemed keen to use it.

I preferred lifts where there wasn't too much conversation as I hated making small talk, but if the driver spoke English and wanted to chat I felt bound to respond in return for the free ride. 'Fair exchange...' as Grandma would have said.

As we got to the outskirts of her town she offered to put me up

138

for the night. I felt uncomfortable about this, preferring to fend for myself. I told her I'd be fine but she insisted, saying it was no trouble. Before I knew it we were pulling up outside her house. Once inside she opened a bottle of wine and organised some food: bread, cheeses, meats, salad and so on. We sat at a table in her kitchen and talked, a little awkwardly at first but as the wine went down we both relaxed and chatted more easily. She told me she was twenty-eight and had done some hitching around Europe when she was younger, so she always felt obliged to pick up hikers when she passed them in her car. I said if I drove I'd do the same. (I doubt if I would though, but I'm saved from that dilemma as I never learned.)

Halfway through the second bottle of wine she asked if I would like to take a shower. I said I was OK but once again, despite my protests, she was adamant. She told me to bring my pack and led me upstairs to her bedroom where the bathroom was en suite. Once she'd explained the eccentricities of the shower controls to me, she gave me a towel and went back downstairs, leaving me to it. Or so I thought.

While I was travelling I usually only got to shower when I stayed on campsites (the exception rather than the rule) where the water was often cold or the pressure inadequate. I didn't mind this too much though, deriving a perverse pleasure from enduring the most spartan of conditions. However it was good to luxuriate in her hot, strong shower with perfumed soap and a warm, fluffy towel waiting for me, so I took my time.

As I stood with my head resting against a tiled wall, letting the steaming water run down my neck and back, I didn't hear the shower door slide open.

"I forgot to give you shampoo," she said.

I nearly jumped out of my skin and was even more shocked when I turned to find her naked, with one foot in the shower stand.

.....

Up to that point in my life I hadn't really had much to do with girls; I was aware of them but never really mixed with them at school. In the time I knew Patrick and Howie they'd never shown much interest in women either. While most teenagers were getting to know the opposite sex (or their own sex) in a frenzy of parties, discos and street corner gatherings, we spent our time in graveyards and darkened rooms talking about the supernatural or UFOs or deciphering the lyrics of some obscure album track.

.....

Celestine was not unattractive and seemed perfectly at ease with her nakedness as she closed the shower door behind her. While we had been sitting at her kitchen table I had no idea that her intentions were anything other than hospitable. I probably would have run a mile if I had. I thought she was just a kind-hearted friendly woman who appreciated the hardships of life on the road.

As she reached out to touch me I flinched violently.

"You are trembling," she pointed out as she ran a fingertip over my chest and arm.

And I was, more from terror than excitement but I think she read it as the latter.

Once we'd washed and returned to the bedroom I owned up to the fact that I was still a virgin, which she found amusing, endearing and thrilling all at the same time. Although I would be amazed if she hadn't already guessed as much; I was still shaking like a leaf and she had to instigate all the action, even to the point of placing my hands on her body.

The next morning, after she had found my camera and posed while I pretended to photograph her, she dressed and went out to get some fresh bread. Lying in bed on my own I considered what had happened. I had certainly been aroused and with her gentle coaxing and other, vigorous means I had reached orgasm. But the experience had been more traumatic than pleasurable and I tried to work out why this should be.

For one thing I was completely inexperienced so, obviously, it was bound to be a bit scary. I also had to try to dispel the sordid images I had stored from years of listening to my mother and her men friends through the bedroom walls. But there was something else: since I was taken away from Dadda I hadn't known any real physical affection, apart from the occasional slobbery kiss from my mother when she was drunk. I had not been touched or held in an intimate, genuinely affectionate way since I was seven years old. So when I found myself naked with a woman for the first time it's no wonder I was traumatised. Never mind sex, the whole idea of physical contact was terrifying.

While I was considering all this, feeling uncomfortable about being there, I heard the front door open and someone moving about downstairs. Assuming it was Celestine I tried to think of a reasonable excuse for making a quick getaway and was just getting out of bed when I heard a man's voice calling, followed by the tread of heavy footsteps on the stairs. With no obvious means of escape and no time to think I pulled the bedclothes over me and pretended to be asleep.

My heart was pounding as the door opened and the man entered the room. After a moment's silence I heard him go over to look in the bathroom and then he spoke. I ignored him at first but he raised his voice, crossing to the bed and shaking me roughly through the blankets. Feigning drowsiness I turned and looked blankly at him. He was a big guy; several years older than me and clearly unhappy. As I stared at him, wondering who he was, he spoke to me again.

"Pardon. Je suis Anglais," I told him, weakly. "Je ne parle pas Francais."

"Anglais?" he sneered, followed by something muttered in French. "What you do here?"

I explained that I had been hitchhiking and that Celestine had given me a lift and let me stay the night as I had nowhere else to go. His English wasn't as good as hers but he seemed to get the gist of what I was saying.

"You sleep here?" he asked, indicating the bed. "With her?"

I wasn't sure if I should lie; although I figured that was probably going to be the best policy. Fortunately I was saved by the sound of the front door opening again. The man glared at me for a few seconds before going back downstairs where I heard him talking to Celestine. Their conversation got a bit heated once or twice and I worried it was going to turn violent but, eventually, I heard the front door slam and a car drive away. As I lay in bed she came into

141

the bedroom.

"You like coffee?" she asked as if nothing had happened.

"Who was that?" I asked.

"My husband," she informed me, blithely. "He live somewhere else now. Separate. Coffee?"

I said coffee would be great and, as soon she had gone down to the kitchen, I dressed hurriedly and re-packed my rucksack. After breakfast she was kind enough to drive me twenty kilometres to a main road where I had a better chance of getting a decent lift; but once she'd gone, as I stood on the roadside, I couldn't help feeling I had been used to get at her estranged husband. Apparently he always came around on that particular day of the week to pick up his mail and I got the distinct impression she wanted him to find me there. I could have been wrong in this assumption; after all, my view of women and their motivations must be heavily influenced by my mother's activities. However, irrespective of Celestine's motives, the point was: she had given me my first sexual experience and I wasn't at all sure how I felt about it.

. . . . .

I had sex with three other women during the years I travelled in Europe. They were all one-night stands and on all three occasions I was very drunk or very stoned, or both. (As were the women.) To such a degree that I remember few details, except: they all took place in tents; they were all initiated by the woman; I failed to get an erection at least once; and I packed up my things and left as soon as possible after each encounter.

That was another attraction of travelling: if I did meet someone and started to get to know them, which happened from time to time, much as I generally preferred my own company, there were never any ties or expectations. We all knew we were going our separate ways within a few days, so no one got too involved.

In all my life I have only had two other sexual encounters; both since I started working at St. Angela's and both with the same prostitute.

On the first occasion she propositioned me as I wandered the streets one night. I don't quite know why I agreed to go with her but I did, following her up some stairs to the dingy back bedroom of a flat over an electrical repairs shop. As I was handing over the money, in advance, I became aware of the sound of a television coming from another room and I realised how thin the walls must have been. I reasoned that, if I could hear the television, then someone in an adjacent room would be able to hear us. Then I started wondering who was watching the television. Could it have been children? Possibly her children? I immediately felt uncomfortable and asked her to stop undressing. She asked whether anything was wrong and I told her I'd changed my mind but she could keep the money. I picked up my coat and left.

Months later, on a warm drizzly night, she recognised me as I was passing on the other side of the street and she called me over. We chatted for a minute or two and she told me she was having a slow night because of the rain. Then she offered to give me a blowjob for free because I hadn't received 'value for money', as she put it, the last time. I said it didn't matter but she insisted and dragged me into an alley. Again, I'm not sure why I let her. She unbuttoned my trousers, stroked me into a state of arousal and began performing oral sex but, after an initial rush of excitement, I started feeling self-conscious and lost my erection. I apologised to her and she told me not to worry about it.

"It happens sometimes," she assured me.

After that I used to see her from time to time when I walked the streets at night. We always said 'Hello' and spoke briefly but sex was never mentioned. I don't know what happened to her. She was a nice woman.

.....

On my final trip to Europe I got a lift for the first and only time into Switzerland. I was dropped off at night on the outskirts of Geneva and, rather than go into the city centre with no currency, I slept under some wooden stairs at the back of an immaculately clean factory. The next morning I was up at daybreak, intending to hitch deeper into the country. I was a patient hitcher most of the time

I travelled in Europe - hardly surprising as I had nowhere in particular to get to - but on this occasion I gave up after four hours. I'd waited much longer in other places but I got the distinct impression that the Swiss drivers in their big shiny cars just didn't see me standing there with my thumb out. So, I made my way into town and caught a local bus that took me back into France; one of the very rare occasions I used any kind of public transport.

In the small French border town I looked for a bank to cash a travellers' cheque and was surprised to find everything closed. I wandered around for a while and eventually found a shop that was open, where I was told it was a public holiday. The lady at the till told me she was about to shut as well and that she wasn't able to cash a cheque for me. I had very little money on me and, while I was happy to sleep rough again that night, I was hungry and fancied a consolatory bottle of wine or two. As I was counting up my handful of francs and centimes to see what I could afford, an elderly lady customer asked, in very good English, if she could help me. I explained my situation and was amazed when she offered to lend me some money and a place to stay for the night. I thanked her, promised to repay her the next day as soon as the banks were open and I picked up an armful of provisions which she paid for. Then she drove us to her home, situated a couple of kilometres outside the town. Almost as soon as the car pulled up the front door of the house opened and an elderly man came out to greet her and help with her bags of shopping. The lady introduced me to her brother, who didn't really speak any English but seemed very happy about my staying there when she explained things. They led me around to their huge back garden, which contained a small orchard, free-range chickens and an outhouse that had been turned into a fully self-contained apartment. The woman told me to make myself at home and to use anything I found, including the contents of the fridge and cupboards. Then they left me alone until late afternoon when she brought me a clutch of fresh eggs and told me that she was leaving for Paris early the next morning, but that I should stay for as long as I wanted.

That evening, after a meal cooked and eaten in the cosy little kitchen, I sat with a bottle of wine on the apartment's veranda and watched the setting sun ignite the snow-capped Alps. For the first time in quite a while I felt a real peace and calm descend on me as I breathed the fresh air, watched the swallows darting among the apple trees and enjoyed the view.

.....

There were lots of mountains in Dadda's stories even though he'd never seen any really big ones himself. During the Second World War he was a conscientious objector and one of the jobs he was put to was cutting down trees for the war effort.

"That's where I learned to love and appreciate wood," he told me. "The lumber was used mainly for pit props in the mines and sleepers on the railroads. Which I suppose was necessary but always seemed like an awful waste of trees to me."

For a while he worked in Snowdonia, the only mountain range he ever saw. On his days off, when he couldn't get home to see Laura, he loved to hike through the forests that covered the hills, climbing above the tree-line and looking down on the valleys spread out below him. He always said he'd love to see the Himalayas or some other major mountain range.

Sitting in the old couple's garden in the south-west of France, appreciating the glory of the Alps, I wished he could have been there sharing it with me.

.....

The next day I cashed a travellers' cheque in town, got my stuff together and went to the old couple's door with the intention of paying back the money the woman had lent me before I hit the road again. But when her brother saw my rucksack and realised I was about to leave he seemed really upset. Although I couldn't make out exactly what he was saying I understood enough to know he was insisting I stay longer. Under normal circumstances once I'd made a decision to get moving I stuck with it, but it occurred to me that the old man might want some company with his sister gone, so I agreed to stay on. It was the least I could do.

Having dumped my pack back in the outhouse I decided I should try to do something tangible to repay them for their kindness. It was early autumn and I noticed that the fruit had started to fall from the trees in the orchard. With the old man's consent I spent the day picking apples, pears and damsons and packing them carefully into the shallow wooden crates he produced from another outbuilding. While I worked among the branches he pottered about at ground level, sorting through the windfalls, only stopping to supply lunch, which we ate together. Our knowledge of each other's language was limited but we managed to make ourselves understood and I felt very much at ease with him.

At the end of the day he gave me a couple of bottles of wine and left me again to my own devices. I spent another pleasant evening on the veranda, although the atmosphere became very heavy and humid during the night – prior to a pre-dawn storm that rattled around the mountains and rumbled across the valley – and I was feasted on by a rogue mosquito.

The next day I finished the fruit picking and did some repairs to the orchard fences, completing the job just as the old lady arrived back from Paris. Her brother welcomed her home and seemed to take great pleasure in showing her the work we'd done. She thanked me for my efforts and invited me join them later in the house for dinner, where she told us about her visit to Paris and gave me a brief history of their home town. She asked me a few polite questions about my travels but never pushed for more details than I wanted to give or tried to pry into my background.

The next morning, despite their further protestations, I decided to leave. I would happily have stayed longer but I didn't want to take liberties with their hospitality. They supplied me with food and wine for my journey and I felt a strange pang of sorrow as I left them, vowing I would try to visit them again the following year. I wasn't to know then that my travelling days were almost over.

.....

I kept my rucksack and battered old tent for five years after my last trip abroad. Every now and then I'd drag them out from under my bed and remember those summers and autumns past, trying to muster some enthusiasm for life on the road, but it wasn't there any more. Or was it that the need for travelling had gone? To a large extent my job at the cemetery had given me the solitude and anonymity I sought and found wandering the highways of Europe. And I no longer had an urge or desire to escape, which had been my primary incentive for leaving in the first place.

2

The periods between my trips to Europe were spent in Britain, working, earning and saving. While I was away I always left enough money in my savings account to keep me going for a couple of weeks once I returned. Just as well because I was often completely broke when I did get back.

Every year I lived in a different town or city, chosen at random as I hitched north from Dover or Folkestone. When I arrived in a place I liked the look of I'd usually check into a hostel for the first few days while I found employment. Then, once I'd got a job, I'd look for somewhere more permanent to live. If I took rented accommodation it was always the most basic I could find, in the sort of building I live in now, where the tenants tend to keep to themselves and the rent is low. But, more often than not I squatted; which I preferred if only for financial reasons. Sometimes I'd manage to find a place of my own but I also stayed in a few established, shared squats.

The jobs I did were usually unskilled manual labour, working in factories, warehouses or on building sites: digging, sweeping, operating machines, loading, unloading, stacking, lifting, carrying. Mindless work that I did at my own pace and rhythm; allowing my brain to shut down and the time to pass quickly.

.....

A good example of the type of work I did was a job I had in a factory that made parts for the car industry. There were various machines – drills, presses, cutters and trimmers - whose functions combined to create these parts out of lumps of metal. I was employed via an agency to operate a new machine, a prototype they were very excited about, which would drill seven separate holes and threads into small brass bars, thus creating single components that would normally take two or three separate processes to produce. All I had to do was dump a load of the brass bars into a shaker which fed them into the machine and then, when the baskets that collected the finished components reached a certain weight, I had to empty them. And that was it.

On my first day I was shown the safe and proper way to do the job, which included stopping the machine every time I changed the baskets. By the first afternoon I was bored with this and realised I could keep the machine running while I changed baskets and still find time to do a bit of sweeping up around the machine. On the morning of my second day I got the machine to churn out more of the components than the previous operator had managed to produce in a whole day. By the afternoon of my third day the machine had broken down - unable to cope with the workload - and I was put to work on a press, but once the machine was fixed I went back to it. After that I kept myself interested by trying to hit new targets each day but, inevitably, the machine would break down after a few days and I'd be put on some other duty. In the end the chief technician requested I be taken off the machine because I was working too hard. I was put in charge of collecting swarf instead.

.....

The one exception to all the dirt and drudgery was when I worked as a lifeguard; a cleaner, easier job but one in which the time dragged. The best part about it was having the pool to myself.

I used to volunteer regularly for the unpopular morning shift when most of the major cleaning was done before the baths were opened to the public. I would arrive early and get my share of the work done so I could swim in the empty pool while the others on the shift were still cleaning or sitting around in the staff room, smoking and drinking tea.

It was almost spiritual as I stood alone on the side of that shimmering blue rectangle, with the water lapping noiselessly against the tiled walls. In the echoey silence of the vaulted building I could hear my breath and heartbeat as I prepared myself, before hurling my body into a high arcing dive. Then the plunge and splash! The rush of liquid, cool against my skin. The other-worldly peace of the length-and-a-half swum underwater. The surfacing and filling of the lungs before the slow, controlled descent, releasing a steady stream of bubbles as the white noise silence closed around me.

The time I spent alone in the pool made up for the boredom of the job where all there was to do was watch the swimmers, blow my whistle from time to time and try to ignore the slow sweep of the huge clock on the deep end wall.

.....

It was in a shared squat that I first smoked marijuana, a couple of years after I left my mother's house. In fact it was in that same year that I was introduced to both drugs and sex, only one of which became something of a habit.

The squat was in a big Victorian house that had about twelve rooms; I'm not sure exactly how many because I never went up to the second floor. My room was on the first floor. As was the case in most of the shared squats I lived in everyone was left pretty much to themselves. There was a big common room on the ground floor where people gathered but there was never any pressure to socialise. I had a battery-operated tape recorder and preferred to stay in my own room, listening to music, drinking cans of beer and reading by the light of a paraffin lamp. I was working in a warehouse at the time, doing as much overtime as I could get, which meant I didn't have to spend too much time at the squat. However the warehouse never opened on Sundays so I had to find other ways to kill the time on my day of rest. Sometimes I'd go to the movies or for long walks or, more often than not, I'd just drink myself to a standstill.

On the Sunday morning in question, a cold winter's day, I woke early with an urge to do something active. I splashed some water on my face, tramped downstairs and went out onto the raised patio at the back of the house. Leaning on the stone balustrade I considered the tangle of grass, bushes, weeds and young trees that was the garden. It was a long, narrow plot and looked as though it had once been attractively laid out; with fruit trees at the far end, borders of flowering shrubs, including several healthy-looking rhododendron bushes, and what I imagined would have been a beautifully manicured lawn. To fully restore it to its former glory would have taken a good deal of time, money and effort but I decided I could at least start the process. As everything was so overgrown there was no obvious place to begin so I just waded in indiscriminately, pulling up and tearing down with my bare hands.

I had been going for some time when I noticed a couple of the guys from the squat standing on the patio, watching me as they drank mugs of steaming tea.

"You're doing a fine job," one called.

"You must be a fucking nutter," the other shouted.

I shrugged and carried on and they soon disappeared. However, maybe twenty minutes later, they reappeared, bringing a rusty old machete, some shears, a spade, a saw and a bacon sandwich.

"We found these," the first guy told me, showing me the tools. "Thought they might come in handy."

"Mind if we chip in?" asked the second. "It looks like a good way of keeping warm."

"It's a free country," I replied.

"Here, we thought you might have worked up a bit of an appetite," said the second guy, Ash, handing me the bacon sandwich.

"Anywhere in particular you want us to start," asked Tony, the other guy.

"Wherever you like," I answered through a mouthful of food. "It all needs cutting back. Just don't go mad with the rhododendrons."

And they joined in; ripping and digging up the undergrowth, hacking and sawing down the overgrowth, all three of us enjoying the work for its own sake. By the middle of the afternoon we had managed to give some basic shape to the garden and we had a huge pile of branches, weeds and manmade junk at the bottom end.

"A job well done," said Tony, resting his weight on a decorative stone birdbath we had unearthed in the middle of the lawn. "We'll be able to have a nice big bonfire in a few days when all that dries out."

"If it doesn't rain," I pointed out.

"Don't be such a pessimist," he replied.

"We're a bunch of regular Inigo Joneses!" called Ash, surveying our handiwork from the patio.

"Capability Brown, you moron!" Tony corrected him.

"Whatever! Come and have a look from up here. It looks great," Ash called back. "And I've got a little reward for everyone," he added, waving a joint above his head.

A couple of minutes later as I held the joint uncertainly I confessed that I'd never even smoked a cigarette before, let alone drugs.

"It's cool, man," Ash informed me. "All you do is breathe it in slowly, just a little bit if you're not sure, then let it sit inside you for a few seconds and breathe it out again."

Which I did successfully, growing in confidence with it as the afternoon wore on and they rolled more joints.

"Who's Capability Brown?" I asked some time later as we sat on the steps leading from the patio down into the garden. To my bemusement the question was met with hysterical laughter.

"I feel more like Incapability Brown," I said in all seriousness, which caused more hysterics.

While the marijuana was reducing them to uncontrollable fits of giggling I found it just dulled my senses, making me feel relaxed and sleepy. But I liked the feeling and quickly got into the habit of smoking dope. When I could get it.

Over the next few weeks the state of the garden continued to improve as some of the others in the squat helped out. One of them got hold of a lawn mower from somewhere and someone else took a gardening book out of the library and did some proper pruning of the trees and bushes. Meanwhile a date was set for Tony's bonfire, which became a real focal point for everyone, creating an increasingly communal atmosphere in the house.

On the night itself we all chipped in to buy food, drink and dope, someone set up their stereo on the patio and, despite the bitter cold, everyone wrapped up and joined in. While most people were dancing and larking about up on the patio I kept an eye on the fire at the far end of the garden, worried that it might get out of control and catch the fruit trees. Unfortunately it wasn't the fire that got out of hand. As the night drew on spirits got a bit too high and when the neighbours complained about the noise, bottles and bricks were thrown and a couple of windows were broken. The police were called and calmed things down but the damage had been done. A couple of days later we were evicted and all went our separate ways.

......

I gave up smoking marijuana not long after I started working at St. Angela's. In the end it was a choice between dope and drink and, as I've always preferred drinking, the dope had to go. This was because I was finding that combining the two had started knocking me about the next day. I could quickly work off hangovers – which I rarely got anyway – but if I'd been smoking as well I could end up fuzzy and unfocused for a whole morning. As someone who takes pride in his work this was not a state I wanted to be in, so I straightened myself out.

......

My constitution toughened up considerably during those periods working in England. I discovered that I could drink hard and still get by with relatively little sleep, as a result of which I developed my habit of wandering the streets at night. Sometimes I went out because I was restless; at other times because I was cold and walking the streets was preferable to lying around in an unheated, unlit room; and sometimes I went out purely because I was interested to see what goes on in a town or city in the dead of night. Things certainly looked different than they did in daylight.

This ability to function without much sleep proved useful one particular year. It was one of the few times I hadn't been able to get regular employment and, because of this, I'd spent far too much money on drink and dope to help fill the empty days of winter.

By the end of April, only a couple of months short of my getaway deadline of July the First, I was well short of my savings target; I wouldn't have lasted more than a few weeks in Europe on what I had in my post office account. I had managed to find work in a factory, injecting liquid rubber into moulds; a messy, hazardous, poorly paid job with two strict shifts, no overtime and, therefore, limited earning potential. It obviously wasn't going to be enough so I decided to take a second job, getting a position as security guard in an office block. My shift at the factory ran from eight a.m. until five-thirty p.m. The security job was ten p.m. to six a.m. For two months I went from one job to the other, rarely going home between the two; the only sleep I got was a couple of hours snatched during the night shift. More often than not I got through the five-day week on a total of ten to fifteen hours' sleep, which I topped up with a solid twelve hours over the weekend. (These days I probably average five or six hours a night, although it's often less.) In those eight or nine weeks, by drinking only at weekends, abstaining from dope and not paying any rent, I saved enough to keep me away for four and a half months. I even brought some money back with me.

3

Twenty-one years after being taken from Dadda's house in Manning Road I found myself back there. It wasn't planned, it just happened that way. I was dropped off a few miles away by a young English couple who were working in Germany for some large international corporation. They were back in England to celebrate the girl's parents' silver wedding anniversary. As I watched them drive away I worked out that it was twenty-nine years since Dadda had married my mother in this town and, for the first time since we left him, it occurred to me that I didn't know if they had ever divorced.

Sitting on my rucksack across the road from Dadda's house I was a little dismayed to see how much had changed over the years. The buildings were the same, structurally, but a block of eight houses in the terrace just along from 163 had all been painted the same pillar box red; I assumed they must have been taken over by a housing association. The walls of all of the front gardens and most of the roofs had been replaced, probably under some local authority scheme. Gates had been fitted at the bottom of all the entries and the trees that ran along the edge of the pavement had recently been pollarded. It all looked a bit stark and unfriendly, not the way I remembered it. This impression was reinforced as I watched the comings and goings on Manning Road; there didn't seem to be any feeling of community like there was when I'd lived there. The people, none of whom I recognised, hardly acknowledged one another as they passed on the street and went in and out of their houses.

After a while I got up and crossed over. I walked past Grandma and Grandpa's old house, past Mrs. Taylor's shop, which was now an estate agents' office, and up Astor Road to St. Michael's where I leaned on the wall and gazed into the empty playground. Simon Stanley. David Shepherd. Danny Keane. I wondered where they were now and what they were doing. I thought about going into the church for a few minutes but, to my surprise, the doors were locked so I made my way to St. Angela's instead.

Passing through the gates things looked much the same as I remembered them. There were some new graves, the trees had grown, the bushes were denser next to the perimeter wall and it was a bit wilder in general but, essentially, it hadn't changed much. I stashed my pack behind a bush just inside the gates and strolled among the graves. It was a bright, warm, late autumn day and, more than ever before at St. Angela's, I noticed the wildlife: birds and squirrels chirping and chattering; bees and wasps enjoying their last days before winter brought a slow, drowsy death; a cat stalking a magpie, which croaked its defiance. I drank some water from a standpipe and slumped against a cool, granite monument. The quiet drone of the insects, the song of the birds and the warmth of the sun made me drowsy; the weariness of travelling flooded through me and I dozed off.

I was woken by the unmistakably lovely sound of a shovel blade biting crisply into earth. Slice. Followed by the dull thud as the load of soil hit the ground. Crump. Slice. Crump. Slice. Crump. Slice. Crump. It had a hypnotic rhythm; a pleasant, soothing monotony.

I got to my feet, crossed to where the gravedigger was working and watched him for a minute or two before greeting him.

"Hello."

"All right," he answered without breaking time.

"Have you been working here long?" I asked.

"I don't work here," he told me with a grunt. "I've just come by today to dig this one."

He heaved another load of earth onto the graveside and stopped, leaning on the handle of his shovel.

"Pass us that bottle will you?" he asked, pointing to a bottle of cordial that was sticking out of a black plastic holdall a few feet from the grave.

I gave him the bottle and asked if he knew Stan.

"Stan? Yeah, I remember Stan. He retired about six years ago now. I've heard nothing of him for a while, mind. Why? D'you know him?" he asked and took a swig of his drink.

"I used to hang around here when I was a kid; a few years ago, now. I used to chat to him sometimes, that's all," I explained.

"Oh, right. Yeah, nice fellow, Stan. They've had a problem replacing him. That's why I'm here."

"You don't usually work here then?"

"No. I work for the council," he told me, wiping the back of his hand across his forehead. "I'm doing this as a favour. Earn a few extra quid."

He took another drink, screwed the top back on the bottle and threw it next to his bag.

"Why? You looking for a job?" he asked.

I realised that I was.

"What qualifications do you need?" I asked.

"A degree in physics," he joked, sinking his shovel back into the soil. He stopped and gave me a look. "Are you serious?"

"Yes."

"If you can stand a bit of hard graft and a few blisters; and if you've got a bit of common sense and a strong back… That's about it. They want someone reliable, mind. That's been the problem with all the blokes since Stan retired; bunch of wasters."

"I'm reliable," I told him.

"Give the priest a knock, then. If he's not there there's a number on the board in the porch," he nodded towards the church. "Give him a call."

And he hefted out another shovelful of earth.

Two days later I started digging my first proper grave; the first I'd dug since I'd buried some animal or other in the back garden of 163 Manning Road. I had a lot to learn and I had to learn it quickly but I was a willing worker. The work was hard at first, after months of doing nothing in Europe, but I soon got to grips with it. Before too long I came to enjoy the labour, losing myself in its steady, mind-emptying rhythm. Slice. Crump. Slice. Crump. Slice. Crump.

.....

When I took the gravedigger's job I had no idea my travelling days were over. At the time I saw it as just another opportunity to earn money for my next trip. But this changed, almost immediately. A combination of moments and resonances led to my decision to settle down. In retrospect I suppose the first would have been when I rested against that monument in St. Angela's; as I drifted into sleep I was filled with a rare sense of contentment, almost as though I had arrived at where I was supposed to get to. And what better final destination than a cemetery?

Another important factor was that this was the only place I could, in any real sense, call 'home'. I was born here. Most of my happy memories are from the time I lived here with Dadda. And I certainly never felt at home in any of the places I lived in after I left Manning Road.

There were other little instances over those first few days – memories triggered and familiarities rediscovered – but the decisive one occurred on the fourth day. As I was crossing the top of Farm Road on my way to St. Angela's I glanced across at 163; it was like seeing through a time slip. A group of five kids were playing in front of the houses, scrambling over the walls and hedges. I stopped and watched them for a minute, drifting into the past as I remembered the games we had played there more than twenty years ago: hopscotch, Grand National, acky-one-two-three. Me and my friends. I snapped out of my daydream when I realised one of the kids was standing on one of the walls, doing a silly dance, shouting abuse and making rude gestures at me. He can only have been about seven or eight.

"No one would have dared make fun of our gravedigger," I thought.

And there he was again, recalled from the days of my childhood. Even though I'd just taken over his job I hadn't thought about him since I was fourteen, but his image was still sharp and clear. As I carried on towards the cemetery I looked down at my clothes – dirty worn-out jeans, desert boots, a couple of tatty old sweat shirts - and I knew immediately what I was going to do.

The following Saturday afternoon I scoured the local rag market, several charity shops and the army and navy store. I went to a chemist's, a tool shop and in a second-hand furniture store I bought a mirror, something I never usually bothered with.

On Sunday I cut chunks out of my long brown hair, bleached it and applied wax to get the spiked effect I wanted. I had managed to find roughly the right clothes and gear: granddad vests; collarless shirts; thick, woollen ex-air force trousers and overcoat; ex-army boots; canvas shoulder bag; and a heart-shaped shovel. The new garb accentuated my tall thin build, although I was not quite as gaunt and haunted-looking as he had been, but when I caught my reflection in a shop window on my way to work on Monday morning I could see it was a good likeness.

4

I got to know Tom about three years after I started working at St. Angela's. The first time we met he'd come to ask about a short notice burial for the following day. He had failed to get Father Courtenay on the telephone so he turned up in person and, finding no one in the presbytery, he wandered into the cemetery where I was cutting back the ivy on the south wall. I didn't have the authority to assign a plot but I told him I'd sort it out with Father Courtenay when he got back and make sure he called Tom to confirm the details.

"How long have you been here now?" he asked.

"About three years," I told him.

"You've certainly made a difference," he said. "The place is looking much better. Tidier. You must be putting in more effort than the other blokes."

The cemetery is just under four square acres and had been more overgrown and untidy than I originally thought when I returned. Once I'd picked up the basic principles of digging graves – taught by Terry, the guy I met on my first day back – I got on with the other aspect of the job: general tidying and upkeep of the grounds. Stan had done his share of these duties while he was here but he wasn't a young man; and he was always more than happy to stop what he was doing to pass the time of day with anyone who cared to chat. His successors seemed to have done very little maintenance work and things had been allowed to run wild, but for me this part of the job has always been more of a pleasure than a chore. I suppose I think of St. Angela's as my garden and over the years I have laboured to get it to a state I can be proud of.

"It's getting there," I told Tom as I looked out across the grounds.

"Well, it's looking pretty good already. Keep up the good work," he said, winking before making his way towards the gates.

.....

Father Courtenay didn't get back until that evening and I ended up digging the grave by the light of an oil lamp. I remember that because it put me in mind of Patrick. If he had seen someone digging in the cemetery at night I'm sure he would have been convinced they were grave robbers or, better still, devil worshippers. Thinking about him put a smile on my face as I toiled in the dark.

.....

I saw Tom at several funerals over the following months and we always smiled and nodded. I liked his round, ruddy face and friendly nature and, if I'm honest, I also liked the fact that he'd noticed and appreciated my work.

The second time we met properly was on a Sunday. It was Dadda's birthday and, as a way of marking it, I was visiting the Lauras' grave, which I had found about eighteen months earlier. As I squatted next to the grave, doing a bit of weeding and giving the stone a wipe, I heard someone stop a few steps behind me.

"What's this? Busman's holiday?" Tom asked, smiling as I turned to him.

"What about you?" I replied.

He laughed.

"Touché! Mad as it might sound, it's my birthday," he told me. "I've come to visit my mother. Funny way to celebrate, eh?"

I smiled weakly, not knowing what to say and there was a moment's uneasy silence.

"So, what about you?" he asked. "Is this someone you know or do you just have an over-developed sense of duty?"

"It's a bit of a long story," I said, evasively.

He nodded, seeming to appreciate that I might not want to talk about it.

"Look," he said, pushing his hands into his coat pockets, "I was going to go for a bit of lunch and a couple of pints down the pub. Do you fancy joining me? Be nice to have a bit of company."

I could easily have said 'no' but there was something about him, a quiet melancholy behind his open friendly nature that put me in mind of Dadda. Plus the fact that they shared a birthday; a coincidence that would be significant when Tom found Dadda years later.

"OK," I said. "Just give me a minute."

I finished tidying the grave and then accompanied him to the pub where our friendship began.

.....

At his invitation I have shared several of Tom's birthdays ever since. Another reason why he gets so irritated that I won't tell him mine.

"What star sign are you?" he asked me one year.

"Dunno," I lied.

"Course you know. Everyone knows what star sign they are, even if they don't read their horoscope. Tell you what: give me three guesses."

"OK."

"Taurus? You're a typical Taurean."

"No."

"No? OK then... Capricorn?"

I shook my head.

"Not Capricorn and not Taurus... Let me think about this."

He was obviously enjoying himself.

"All right then... Bit of a long shot maybe... Virgo!"

"Wrong again," I told him flatly.

"I don't know why I'm bothering. You wouldn't tell me even if I got it right, would you?" he asked grumpily before stomping off to the toilet.

I would have told him if he'd been right; I don't like lying unnecessarily. It's funny because it obviously never occurred to him that we shared a star sign. So much for astrology.

.....

Over the years, Tom and I shared secrets and details about our lives, although him more so than I.

He is seventeen years older than me. While I was a child in the nineteen sixties he was coming to terms with his sexuality. He knew from an early age that he was gay and once he was old enough he started to explore the gay lifestyle.

"It was all very clandestine and a bit seedy back then," he told me. "Exciting in one respect but very scary in another. I lived in constant fear of being discovered and exposed. I was terrified in case it ever got back to my mother. I don't think she would have coped. I loved her dearly and she loved me but... she wouldn't have understood. She was very old fashioned. It would have destroyed her. And that would have destroyed me."

Eventually the stress started affecting his health and he decided the only answer was denial.

"By the time Mother died, I'd got used to the idea of celibacy.

I can't imagine being intimate with someone now."

His colleagues at the funeral directors thought he was an eccentric old-fashioned bachelor and, as far as he was aware, no one else knew about his past. Unfortunately this assumption proved incorrect.

"Anyway, I'm quite happy with my birds," he told me.

Which was something of an understatement. He loved birds. The back bedroom of his house was a walk-in aviary where he kept canaries and finches.

"I love to sit with them," he told me once. "It's so… special. 'Uplifting', that's the word I'm looking for. Listening to their songs. Watching them fly around. Feeling them land on my shoulders or my head or my hands. Nothing can touch that. It's the most beautiful feeling in the world."

There was a contented faraway look on his face as he nursed his pint and thought about his birds.

He was a member of several ornithological organisations and went on regular birdwatching trips around the British Isles and, occasionally, abroad. He had a few birdwatching friends that he hooked up with from time to time but, in the main, he preferred to keep himself to himself. Just as I did.

Ours was an easy, uncomplicated friendship. We might go weeks without seeing each other but when we did our routine changed little: we drank beer and chatted quietly, with Tom doing most of the talking. We both understood there were no fixed arrangements and no obligations.

5

I don't know if any of Laura's relatives still live in the area but, if they do, they obviously don't visit her grave. It was a miracle I ever found it, it was so overgrown with grass and weeds. Dadda would have been mortified if he'd seen the state of it. The day I uncovered it I did what tidying I could and returned the following evening, armed with the appropriate tools to do a proper job. When I had finished I stood back and pictured myself sitting there with Dadda all those years ago on the anniversary of the Lauras' deaths. I wondered what they would be like if they were still alive. And then I wondered about Dadda; whether he was still alive. And if he was still alive where he was and what he was doing.

I never thought, not even in my wildest dreams, that I would see him again.

.....

When I started at St. Angela's I had to clean and sharpen all of the tools I inherited with the job. They had not been properly cared for and, because of the ramshackle condition of the shed they were kept in, the weather had got at them, leaving them blunt and rusty. I realised that if I wanted them to last I'd have to do something about the shed, so its renovation was one of the first major tasks I attended to.

I convinced Father Courtenay that it was an essential job, both for the enduring life and security of the tools and also for my sake, as I needed somewhere to spend my breaks in bad weather. I was hoping he would pay out for new timber but he had other ideas; he had heard there might some to be had for free. An old amateur theatre in the area was being stripped out for refurbishment and he suggested I go and see what I could find. As it turned out the timber I got there was better than anything the church would have forked out for from a timber merchant.

.....

Father Courtenay is a plump, jovial man in his early forties. He likes his food, has been known to take a drink and he smokes like a chimney. He is also extremely thrifty and always on the lookout for a bargain. If I've been working somewhere between the gate and the presbytery he's often interrupted me on his way back from the shops, bringing over the purchases he's just made so he can show me the deals he's picked up. He probably knows I couldn't care less about it but he can't help himself showing off his 'business acumen', as he calls it.

"If I hadn't received the call, Mason, I could have been a tycoon," he never tires of telling me.

I once asked him if avarice wasn't a sin.

"Prudence and avarice are very different things," he replied sternly. "Being careful with money is no sin."

"I thought money was the root of all evil," I challenged him.

"No. No. It's the love of money that's the root of all evil, Mason. It's a different thing entirely. I don't love money; I respect it. And I'm careful with it. And 'many a mickle makes a muckle', as they say."

He has been at St. Angela's almost as long as I have now and he's very popular with the congregation. For the first year or so, when he learned about my lack of faith, he always tried to steer our conversations around to religion; at which point I always remembered a job I had to do on the other side of the cemetery. Eventually he stopped bothering me. He was satisfied with the work I did and he left me in peace, most of the time, to get on with it.

.....

Beneath layers of warped plywood and cracked linoleum the theatre's stage was made of tongued-and-grooved oak boards. The guys doing the stripping, casual labourers earning a bit of cash-in-hand, had no idea of the quality of the wood. They were more than happy for me to spend time carefully prying up the boards with a crowbar while they had their lunch break.

Bill Barlow, a local builders' merchant and parishioner of St. Mike's, picked up the boards in his truck and delivered them to St. Angela's that afternoon. He also lent me some woodwork tools. With such excellent raw materials to hand I was keen to do a job Dadda would have been proud of. Taking care and time I chose not to use nails or screws in the construction of the frame, putting to use my underemployed joinery skills instead. I treated the boards before fixing them and when it was finished the whole thing was as solid as a rock, with perfect weather-proofing that has stood me in good stead ever since. There are no cracks for wind or rain to get in, it gives me shade from the sun in summer and, warmed by a small paraffin heater, is a cosy retreat in winter.

It will be a shame to burn it down but, at the same time, I think it is a fitting last resting place for Dadda and me.

.....

In all the time since I was taken away from Dadda I never stopped thinking about him. Odd little things would bring him to mind at unexpected moments and, obviously, over the last ten years I have been living with constant reminders. But certain things, such as whittling and rebuilding the shed – using the skills that he used every day of his working life – gave me a strong sense of connection with him; a closeness. It was a terrible shock, then, when I found out how close I have been to him for the last six years.

6

I couldn't say what I think about while I'm working. I spend a certain amount of time in the mornings planning what jobs I'll do that day and how I'll go about them but once I'm involved in a job, especially digging graves, I have no idea what goes on in my head.

It takes two to three hours to dig a grave, depending on the time of the year and the state of the soil. Being a perfectionist I know that I am conscious of making the lines of the hole clean and true, which requires a certain amount of concentration; but when I'm just shifting soil, lost in the rhythm of the work, my mind is a blank.

I do have an imagination, although it's rarely used to anything like its full potential these days. In a creative sense anyway. One period of my life when it was exercised was during the months and years after I was beaten up, when I dreamt up violent revenges. Five years into my life as a gravedigger I was presented with an opportunity to realise those dreams.

.....

A mile and a half from my bedsit, in the opposite direction to Manning Road, is a reservoir. It's open to the public during the hours of daylight and is a popular recreation area, with picnic tables and benches dotted about the place and a sandy path running around the lake. On nice days it attracts crowds of people, there to enjoy the open air and feed the waterfowl. The swans and geese are particularly friendly, or brave, swimming into the shallows to accept food direct from the hands of wary adults and excitable children, while the ducks and moorhens squabble further offshore, waiting for crusts to be thrown out to them. There are usually a fair few anglers there too, trying to coexist with the bird feeders and the dog-walkers and the stone- and stick-throwers. I have seen the odd outburst when the disturbances have become too much for the fishermen but, in the main, the 'resa', as it's known locally, is a peaceful idyllic setting.

I had never considered trying to get into the 'resa' after dark until I found myself desperate for a pee one night while I was walking the streets. I wandered down a dirt track that runs along one side of the reservoir's perimeter and, as I was relieving myself, I noticed a break in the chain link fence where it had been ripped away from the trunk of a sycamore tree. Once I'd buttoned myself up I squeezed through the gap, pushed through a tangle of shrubs and emerged on the path a few yards from the water's edge.

It was a cloudy night, with very little light from either moon or stars, but I could just about make out the outlines of things around me. I took a can of beer from my coat pocket and sat on a low wooden bench, enjoying the darkness, the quiet and the clean cool breeze that was drifting across the reservoir. It was hard to believe I was still in the environs of a large town.

After a while I heard an owl hooting somewhere off to my right and I got up to investigate. As I followed the path, passing a large clump of bushes, I noticed a lamp shining further along the shore. I approached cautiously and was able to make out the figure of a man sitting under a large umbrella, surrounded by fishing paraphernalia. He remained still and silent for quite some time, facing out over the water, and I wondered if he was asleep; but then he moved, raising a can to his lips and drinking deeply.

.....

I've never had any real inclination to go fishing. I don't know why because I probably have the right temperament for it.

Big Mick used to fish. On one of our daytrips Dadda and I went to meet up with him when he was having a few days' fishing holiday, camped on the bank of a river somewhere.

"It's great, Mason," he told me enthusiastically. "I can sit here all day and night, enjoying the peace and the fresh air, waiting for a tickle with no one to bother me. Not even the missus. Especially not the missus!" he joked.

"But, what do you do?" I asked.

It all sounded very boring.

"What I've just said," he explained. "Appreciate the countryside."

"Oh!" I wasn't impressed.

"And if I fancy a bit of company there's a pub just along the way," he said, nodding towards a bend in the river.

"Can we go to the pub now?" I asked, with crisps and a bottle of pop in mind.

Dadda and Big Mick both laughed.

"One day, Mason, when you're older," said Mick. "Maybe you'll understand then."

"Look!" exclaimed Dadda, grabbing my arm and pointing across to the opposite bank where a heron was swooping in to land in the shallows. "He's come fishing, too."

"How does a bird fish?" I asked.

"Watch," Dadda whispered.

For the next twenty minutes or so I forgot about the pub and watched, fascinated; waiting and hoping that the heron would spear a fish in the way Big Mick described it. It didn't, and Mick didn't catch any while we were there either, but it was a lovely day; warm and lazy, with the sun sparkling on the water and Dadda and Big Mick taking time to point out things to me; making me realise that sitting quietly and observing could be just as enjoyable as running about, or playing on swings and roundabouts, or watching television.

.....

Having drained his drink the fisherman twisted heavily on his stool and lobbed the can into a rubbish bin just behind him. The sound as it landed was the thin clunk of aluminium hitting aluminium. When I looked in the bin as I was leaving, a while later, there was a whole pile of empty super-strength lager cans in there.

(There was a time when I used to drink that stuff. I stopped when it occurred to me that anyone drinking something as strong as that isn't doing it for enjoyment.)

I watched him for a few more minutes, during which time he gave no indication that he was aware of my presence, before I moved closer.

"Caught anything?" I asked.

He turned to look at me but he didn't answer. Instead he reached down into a carrier bag, pulled out another can of lager, opened it, took a swig and stared out over the water again. I assumed he didn't want to talk so I turned to walk away.

"Where's your pitch?" he asked, without looking at me.

"I'm sorry?" I replied.

"Where's your stuff? Your rods and that?"

"I haven't got any," I told him. "I don't fish."

"What you doing here then? This time of night?"

It must have been about 2.30 a.m.

"Just walking. Thinking… You know…"

"Mmmm!" He seemed to accept this. "Want a drink?"

He offered me his can.

"I've got my own, thanks," I replied.

I pulled a can from my pocket and opened it. We were silent for a while, drinking and looking out into the darkness. Eventually he offered me his basket to sit on but I declined, saying I ought to be going as I had to get up for work in the morning.

"What do you do?" he asked.

"Labourer," I told him, bending the truth slightly. I don't like giving away too much about myself.

"You like your job?" he asked.

"Yes, I do," I answered honestly.

"You're a lucky man then," he said, bitterly. Then, after a moment: "What you doing here, anyway? I've never seen you before."

"Just enjoying the fresh air," I explained again, realising he was very drunk. "Anyway, I should be going…"

"Yeah. See you around," he said before drinking thirstily from his can of super-strength lager.

Throughout this whole exchange the lamp was on the ground beyond him, so his face remained in shadow and I didn't get a good look at him. But the next time I found him there I got to see him clearly and recognised him immediately.

…..

I did catch a fish once, possibly an eel; something big and long anyway.

It happened one evening in a small port in northern Italy. As I walked along the pier I found some old discarded fishing tackle and, without really knowing what I was doing, I decided I'd give it a go. I stuck a bit of spicy sausage on the hook, dropped it into the water and leant against a wooden railing to watch the sun setting over the sea. I didn't really expect to catch anything, so I was a bit over-excited when I got my first couple of nibbles and I almost went flying as I yanked the empty hook out of the water. But I learned quickly and by the third time I was more prepared. I felt a gentle tug on the line, waited patiently until it started to go taut and then I pulled hard. Bingo! Except that, stupidly, I had wrapped the line around the first two fingers of my right hand and as the fish struggled the line tightened, biting into my flesh. I was in agony as the line cut deeper but I was determined not to lose the fish and, after wrapping a handkerchief around my left hand, I managed to haul it clear of the water. Hanging over the railing I could see down to where it was flapping and twisting in the air; a long silvery brown thing with a gaping pink mouth. It wasn't until I'd got it nearly level with the decking that I stopped to ask myself what I was going to do with it. I had no idea if it was edible or how to go about gutting and preparing it even if it was. I thought about this for a few seconds before unraveling the line from around my fingers and dropping the fish back into the sea.

The fishing line had cut right down to the bone and I probably should have had stitches but I had no insurance and couldn't afford to pay medical costs. Instead I managed to staunch the bleeding by wrapping the wounds in cloth and sitting for an hour or so with my arm held above my head. Over the three or four weeks the wounds took to heal I kept them clean and, in lieu of antiseptic, staved off infection by pouring white wine over them. I still have a neat thin white scar around each of my fingers. Amazingly, considering some of the jobs I've done over the years and the drunken, doped-up states I've got myself into, they are the only scars I have.

.....

When I saw him again he was in the same spot, next to the rubbish bin on the shore of the 'resa'. After a bit of prompting he seemed to remember our first meeting and this time I accepted his offer of the fishing basket.

At first I was the one who made most of the conversation, such as it was. I mentioned again how peaceful it was and asked if that was why he came fishing at night; and did he catch much. His answers came in the form of grunts and nods and shrugs. He was drinking heavily and finished four cans of super-strength lager in the time it took me to drink two cans of weaker beer.

"You married?" he asked suddenly, apropos of nothing.

"No."

"Hmmm!"

"You?" I inquired.

"Was. Yeah. Still am, I suppose." He thought about this for a while. "Got no kids then?"

"No," I replied.

From the way he asked I was fairly sure he had kids and I assumed that was where the conversation was leading, but he changed the subject abruptly.

"I used to be a footballer," he said. "Good one. Semi-pro. You play?"

I told him I wasn't much of a sportsman.

"Yeah. I was good," he continued. "Had a couple of clubs watching me."

He went on to tell me about the teams he had played for, games he had played in, goals he had scored and medals and trophies he had won.

"Player of the year two seasons running," he concluded proudly, savouring the memory before falling into a brooding silence.

I watched him, silhouetted against the light from his lamp. I could only see his face in profile – flattened Roman nose, sloping forehead and weak chin – but I imagined there may have been the glisten of a tear on his cheek. After a minute he opened another can, took a long gulp and leaned drunkenly to his right. When he straightened up he had a walking stick in his hand.

"Fucking good player. And then this happened."

He swung the stick violently, hitting his left foot and making me start backwards.

"Didn't feel a thing," he said, laughing. "Listen..."

He hit the foot again, less violently this time. The blow made a strange, hollow sound.

"It's plastic mate. I'm like the Bionic fucking Man. Only difference is, he wasn't a fucking cripple."

He took another hefty swig of lager.

"Lost it when I was eighteen, working in a factory. It was one of the lads' birthday and a few of us snuck out early before lunch and went down the pub. The foreman was a decent bloke and clocked our cards for us. He liked me 'cos I was top goal scorer for the works' team. Then another bloke clocked us back in while we stayed in the pub a bit longer; so we had a good couple of hours' boozing. Anyway, when we got back we did a bit of work and then we started mucking about, and the kid whose birthday it was challenged me to a forklift race around the yard."

He guzzled the rest of his can and threw the empty at the bin, missing completely.

"Race around the yard... I left him standing. I was pissing on him; up out of me seat, turning around giving him the 'V's. It was all a big laugh."

He opened another can.

"Then it just went. Hit something...? Skidded on some oil...? I don't know. I can't remember. The whole thing turned over and this was crushed..."

He poked his foot gently with the end of the walking stick.

Almost like he was checking to see if the sensation might have returned.

"It's all I ever thought about; playing football. I was good too."

We sat in silence for a while until I finished my can and got up to put it in the bin. As I stooped to pick up the can he had thrown there was a crash behind me. I turned to see he had fallen off his stool and was struggling to get up, so I went to help him.

"Get off! Get off me!" he snarled, pushing me away. "I might be a cripple but I'm not fucking useless. I can do things for myself you know, despite what she says."

He tried to get up but slipped and fell flat on his face. As I reached out again to give him a hand he turned towards me; and towards the lamp beside me.

"Fuck off!!" he screamed.

His face was contorted with anger and frustration: his eyes bulged; his mouth was a spit-flecked vicious slit; and the scar, running from the corner of his right eye down across his stubbly ruddy cheek, shone silver in the bright white light of the gas lamp.

It was like a flashback in a film. In an instant the whole episode ran through my head: the back slang; the push into the hedge; the kicks and punches; and the glimpse of their faces as I tried to protect myself.

I stepped back. 'It couldn't be him, could it?'

I watched him drag himself back onto his stool and raise his drink to me.

"Didn't spill a drop," he laughed, trying to make light of the incident.

Once he'd settled down I took another can of beer from my pocket and sat on the grass next to the lamp so I could get a good look at him.

"Are you OK?" I asked.

"Course I am. Hard as bricks, me," he slurred and drank deeply again.

There followed another silence during which he pulled faces at nothing in particular while running a finger around the lip of his can.

"Have you always lived around here?" I asked.

171

"Born and bred," he replied.

I couldn't ask straight out if he was the one who had beaten me up all those years ago so I was digging around for clues that would confirm it for me.

"How did you get the scar?" I asked.

He brought his hand unsteadily to his face – the alcohol was starting to affect him noticeably now – and ran his thumb down the length of the scar, tracing it with familiarity.

"War wound," he said.

"Sorry?"

"Gang fight. Kid with a bottle fucking slashed me."

He drank again, wobbling visibly on his stool as he did.

"What was the fight about?" I asked, trying to steer the conversation towards the questions that might give me my answer, but his eyes were closing and his head was lolling forward onto his chest.

"Kid fucking slashed me," he mumbled. "I got him though… I got him…"

And he was gone; spark out on his stool. I watched him dribbling and snoring and tried to convince myself this wasn't him; but deep down I was sure he was. After a few minutes I turned down the lamp to a glimmer, took his half-empty can from his hand, placed it on top of the basket and made my way home.

…..

I don't remember Dadda having any scars but he did have a split thumbnail. Long before I was born he'd hit it with a hammer, damaging it badly. It had never repaired properly and always grew back with the split down the centre, the two halves overlapping slightly.

"Does it hurt," I asked once, holding his thumb gently as I inspected the nail.

I was sitting on his lap on the shed step.

"It did for a while," he answered.

"How did you do it?"

"I was careless."

"Careless? Is that what you call it?" asked Big Mick, who was standing in the middle of the lawn with a big grin on his face. "You've not been 'careless' at work since, have you Stephen?" he added, jiggling his mug of tea as you might jiggle an empty pint glass.

Dadda smiled back at him.

"That was a long time ago Mick and we both know the reason. I learned my lesson."

"Yeah. Knocked a bit of sense into you, I'd say. And not before time too," said Big Mick. "I think your Dadda's brains must be in his thumb, Mason. And you want to remember, son: 'where there's life there's hope'. Isn't that right, Stephen?"

"Depends on your definition of 'life,' Mick," Dadda replied.

"Aah, don't get started on all that!" said Mick, scornfully.

I didn't have a clue what they were talking about. I looked at Dadda who smiled reassuringly.

"It doesn't hurt any more though," he said and gave me a hug.

.....

"I got him back, though; a couple of months later. Me and a mate got him on his own and gave him a right good kicking. Put him in hospital."

I had gone back to the reservoir again. I had to know for certain if this was him.

After a couple of drinks he was quite happy to talk about his violent past. He told me he had been in a gang who had a running 'turf war' with a rival gang from a neighbouring district. The lad who gave him the scar was a member of this other gang.

"How old were you?" I asked.

"I don't know... Fifteen? Sixteen?"

I sat on the ground, twiddling a blade of grass as I worked out how to get to the question I wanted answering.

"Did you ever fight with people who weren't from the other gang?"

He stood up and hobbled over to the water's edge.

"Probably," he said, undoing his fly. "I don't remember. I suppose..."

"Or just beat people up?" I asked.

173

He grunted and started to pee into the reservoir.

"Yeah, maybe. Sometimes. I suppose if we saw someone we didn't know; or if we didn't like the look of them; and we fancied a bit of a laugh… Yeah, we might, you know, rough 'em up a bit. Just for a laugh though. It didn't mean anything."

"But you wouldn't remember them, though?"

"No. Why should I? Like I said: it didn't mean anything."

I thought about this while he continued to pee. I was sure who he was now. All the evidence was there: as well as the scar he was the right age, he had lived in the right area and he had the mindless aggressive personality I would have expected. And it was clear that, as far as he was concerned, beating me up had just been a bit of fun. He dismissed as 'meaningless' something that affected my life for years. He disgusted me.

When he turned, zipping up his trousers, I stared at him for a second with memories of daydreams running through my head. I had to get away from him. I got up and walked quickly towards the gap in the fence.

"Where you going?" he called.

I couldn't answer him. Couldn't speak to him.

I didn't sleep that night. I lay on my bed thinking about him. Imagining him drunk, slumped unconscious on his stool with drool trickling from a corner of his mouth. It would be the easiest thing in the world to kill him. A knife. A wire around the throat. A blow to the back of the skull.

I knew he lived alone, estranged from his wife and daughter; that he had few friends; that he was a loner who picked up bits of casual work to supplement his disability allowance. No one knew he came fishing at night. And no one would miss him. Not for a while at least.

I let my imagination run on, taking things to the next stage, working out how to dispose of his body. I could lash him to his basket with fishing line, tow him out to the centre of the reservoir and load the basket with rocks to drag him under. I'd have to take out the rocks a few at a time, which would be a bit laborious, but it should work. The reservoir was pretty deep so there was little chance of him being seen from the shore as he hung, weighted to the bottom.

Before I knew it it was time to go to work; but even there, while I got on with my jobs, I found myself still thinking about it. It wasn't until I got home that evening that I stopped to consider what it was that I was planning. I was shocked, just as I had been as a teenager, when I realised how involved I had become in the whole idea.

.....

Pushing Corbin around the classroom and throwing the chair at him were impulsive acts, over which I had no control. What I was contemplating now was premeditated cold-blooded murder. Could I have gone through with it? I don't think so. I don't think I'm a killer. As it turned out matters were taken out of my hands anyway.

.....

I found him at the reservoir three more times.

On the first two occasions my planned revenge niggled at the back of my mind while I sat with him and I was very aware of potential weapons – his knife, a length of fishing line, a hefty-looking log under a bush near the bin – that I could use to carry out his murder.

I thought about confronting him with the fact that he had beaten me up to see what his reaction would be, to see if he showed any remorse, but I never seemed to find the right moment. Instead I listened to him telling me what a mess his life was. How he had ruined everything: his football career; his marriage; his relationship with his daughter; friendships. Except, the way he told it, his misfortunes were all somebody else's fault. There was always someone else to blame; usually his wife. The only times he ever laughed were with irony or cruelty. He was a sad, pathetic man: consumed by resentment with a grudge against the whole world. Killing him would almost have been a kindness.

The last time I found him was on a clear night with a full moon and a good sprinkling of stars about. When I got to the 'resa' his gear was in the usual place – his lamp was lit, his fishing lines were in the water and, judging by the contents of the bin, he had already got through a fair amount of lager – but he was nowhere to be seen. I assumed he had gone for a pee so I sat on his basket and scoured the night sky, trying to locate the three constellations I recognise.

After a few minutes I got up and checked around in the bushes but there was still no sign of him. I wasn't worried about him, just curious about where he might have disappeared to. Returning to the shore I scanned the surface of the moonlit reservoir and saw a dark shape floating about thirty yards out. I couldn't be sure it was him; but then I couldn't think what else it might be. I watched for a few seconds, straining to see if he was moving. I had no idea how long he had been there, or if he was dead or alive; the only way of knowing would be to swim out to him. But why should I? What did I care if he was drowned? Or drowning? 'Good riddance to bad rubbish' as far as I was concerned. But then I thought about his daughter: even if they were estranged he was still her father.

I undressed quickly and swam out. He was floating face down when I got to him and there was no sign of life when I turned him onto his back. I towed him to the shore where I checked his pulse but he was dead. I thought about giving him mouth-to-mouth or heart massage but I couldn't bring myself to do it. Despite years of working in the 'Death Business', as Tom called it, this was the first time I had seen a human corpse.

I looked him over to see if there were any signs that he might have fallen or hit his head but there were no visible cuts or bruises. I wondered what had happened? Had he drowned himself? Did he have an accident? Or was he struck down by a heart attack or a stroke or something? I had no way of knowing and I never found out.

The next thing to consider was whether or not I should tell the police. And if so should I do it anonymously or identify myself and try to help with their inquiries? In the end I decided it was too risky as I would almost certainly come under suspicion if foul play was suspected. I lay him face down in the shallows and hooked one of his feet over a root so he wouldn't float away again. Someone else could find him in the morning. I got dressed, made sure there was no evidence of my being there and I left. I have never been back since.

.....

Despite all my murderous plans I found no satisfaction in his death. No sense of justice having been done or vengeance being exacted. If I had any strong feelings about the incident it was pity for his daughter.

The question I have asked myself, without ever being able to give an honest answer, is whether or not I would have kept going to meet him at the reservoir if he hadn't drowned? Would I have carried on listening to him moaning about the hardships and injustices of his miserable life? Seeing the bitterness and hostility etched on his face, as clear as his scar, in the harsh light of the gas lamp? And if I had kept going: why?

.....

Until a few days ago I had never seriously considered suicide. The idea has crossed my mind from time to time but I have never thought about it with any real conviction. I once asked Tom if he ever had.

"No. Why should I? Life's pretty good really. Why? Have you?" he asked.

"No," I replied. "I could do it. I'm not afraid of dying."

"No, nor am I," he said. "But that's not the point."

"No, I suppose not."

"I think you'd have to get into a pretty desperate state before it came to killing yourself. And I'm too much of an optimist. No matter how bad things get you never know what's just around the corner."

Prophetic words, if only he'd known it.

7

I was in my usual seat in the bar of the Grouse And Gun one

Saturday evening, about four months ago. I had a book open on my lap but my mind had wandered and when Tom arrived I was staring blankly at the flashing lights of a fruit machine.

"Wakey wakey!" he chirped, nudging my shoulder.

I snapped out of it and greeted him. I hadn't seen him for a couple of weeks.

"Where were you?" he asked.

"I don't know. Miles away…"

"I've got some news for you," he told me. "Pint?"

"Don't see why not," I replied, rubbing my face to waken myself up and wondering what news he could possibly have.

When he got back with the drinks he came straight to the point. He had been at Fairfields, a local old people's home, the previous day to collect one of the residents who had passed away.

"I was walking through with one of the nurses, going to open up the back doors. I hadn't been up there for a few months and we were having a bit of a natter. She's retiring soon. Nice woman. Anyway, as we passed one of the rooms she noticed this old chap putting his coat on.

"And where do you think you're going, Mr. Preskett?" she asked and went in to settle him down.

"I didn't think too much about it at first but when she came out I asked what his Christian name was and she told me it was Stephen. I still thought it was probably just a coincidence but I asked if she knew when his birthday was. She checked his records and guess what?"

I knew what he was going to say.

"Same as mine," he confirmed.

I think I went into shock. Part of me hoped he was joking but I knew he wouldn't joke about something like that. I should have been pleased and excited but I wasn't; I was scared.

I stared at him and then back at the winking lights of the fruit machine.

'Jackpot'. 'Jackpot'. 'Jackpot'. 'Jackpot'.

"Do you want a Scotch?" he asked.

…..

Just as a series of incidents helped me decide to leave my mother, so a set of circumstances, over which I have had no control, has led me to the point where I am about to take Dadda's life and my own. Looking back now I can identify that night in the pub as the moment when everything started to change. Until then my life had a pattern, or structure, built around constants that I could accept and rely on; over the last four months the foundations of that structure have been severely shaken.

I have never had a problem with the concept or the reality of 'death' but these circumstances have put me in a position where, for the first time, I have been made to question my definition of 'life'.

.....

Thirty years with no news of my Dadda. Just memories. The only tangible things I had to remind me of him were his carvings and the camera he bought for me. Those and the occasional evocative whiff of a certain brand of pipe tobacco.

The Mason he had known was a young boy with bright inquiring eyes and laughter in his voice. What expectations might he have had for me? What dreams? And what had I done with those three decades? What did I have to show for them? A handful of qualifications I have never used; some albums of obscure photographs; a small selection of my own carvings; one person I called a friend; and a job burying the dead.

Would he be proud of me?

.....

The matron led me down a corridor.

"We thought he had no relatives," she said. "Not locally anyway."

"He's my stepfather," I explained. "I haven't seen him for a long time. We lost touch."

"It's easy done these days, isn't it? They say all this technology's making the world a smaller place but I don't know. It's just getting more crowded as far as I can see. Anyway, it'll do him good. Might perk him up a bit. He's never had a visitor before, the whole time he's been here."

I didn't like the smell of the place; a mixture of disinfectant, polish, institutional cooking and the unmistakable indefinable odour of old people. When we got to Dadda's room she breezed straight in without knocking or showing any other sign of consideration.

"Oh! He's not here. He must be in the day room," she said, turning me around to retrace our steps. She was a no-nonsense sort of person who seemed as though she was always in a hurry.

As we got back into the entrance hall the front doorbell rang.

"I'll just have to get that," she said. "The day room's down there, on the left. At the end." She pointed along another passage. "You go ahead. I'll pop along in a minute." And she bustled off.

My heart was racing as I walked slowly to the end of the corridor and looked through the wired-glass pane in the door. There was a television set on in one corner of the room but no one seemed to be taking any notice of it; the shelves and windowsills were dotted with ceramic ornaments and vases filled with plastic flowers; there were a few pictures and a couple of brass-framed mirrors hanging on the flock-papered walls; and there were about twenty orange or lime green plastic armchairs scattered around the room, some of which were occupied.

I went in and looked around at the faces. Two elderly ladies were chatting across a coffee table laden with magazines. There were two other old women and three old men seated solitarily around the room but Dadda wasn't there.

I smiled at one of the ladies who had looked over at me and I turned to leave just as the matron came into the room.

"Found it all right then? You've got a visitor, Mr. Preskett," she said to someone behind me.

I turned around and looked at the old man she was addressing.

"Mr. Preskett?!" she spoke louder. The old man looked up and stared at her blankly. "Visitor, Mr. Preskett."

This wasn't Dadda! This old chap was small and shrivelled; his face was pinched and hollow; and his hair, what little he had left, was grey and white around the piebald dome of his head. He bore no resemblance to the man I remembered sitting on the shed step, carving wood and telling me stories. I almost told the matron there had been some mistake but, at the last second, I noticed his hands gripping the thin pinewood arms of his armchair.

"You all right then?" she asked. "I've got to get on, if you don't mind. You can take him back to his room if you want a bit of privacy; his name's on the door. But come and find me before you go, so we can have a little chat."

I thanked her and sat next to the old man.

"Dadda?"

There wasn't even the slightest flicker of recognition at the sound of his name. I gently pried the fingers of his left hand free from the chair arm and looked at his thumb; the nail was split down the middle.

"Dadda? It's me; Mason. Mason? Remember?"

He looked down at his hand in mine and then back at my face. Nothing.

I stayed with him for about half an hour, talking to him, reminding him of things we had done together, trying to get some kind of response out of him, but with no luck. He sat silent and motionless; his only movement an occasional unconscious tugging at the lapels of his jacket.

Dadda wasn't there.

. . . . .

When I found the Lauras' grave, eight or nine years ago, I tried to imagine what they would have been like if they'd still been alive. In my mind's eye I saw them as a young woman and a little girl; despite the fact that they had both died fifteen years before I was born and that little Laura would have been about the same age as my mother. In the same way, I had never pictured Dadda as being any different. In my imagination he was frozen in time. I expected him to be the same as I remembered him so it was quite a shock to find he had changed so much.

. . . . .

The matron filled me in on what little they knew about him.

His brother Ted had died six years earlier and Dadda returned from Australia shortly afterwards, moving into a house in Harding Road. Harding Road is two streets behind Manning Road, running parallel to it between Rufus Road and Astor Road. He lived there for four years until he had a fall and broke his hip. Apparently he lay at the foot of his stairs for a whole day before a neighbour found him. While he was in hospital social services were called in to see him and it was decided that he was too frail, mentally and physically, to look after himself. The sale of his house and his financial affairs were taken care of and when he was released from hospital he was taken to Fairfields.

"He's no trouble at all," the matron told me. "Very quiet."

"Does he ever speak?" I asked.

"Sometimes he mutters away to himself but he doesn't really talk to anyone. Or mix with the other residents. He wanders about the place, though. And he's forever putting his coat on and trying to get out."

"Is he allowed out?"

"Oh, yes. He gets taken out from time to time."

"No. I mean; could I take him out sometime?"

"I don't see why not," she said. "It'd probably do him good."

"OK, good. But, as far as you know, he doesn't remember anything?" I asked.

"It's hard to say. Sometimes they remember things that happened years ago, in incredible detail; and then they'll forget what they've just had for breakfast. With your stepfather, because he doesn't really communicate, there's no way of knowing what's going on in his head. But, you never know, you might bring him out of himself a bit. It happens sometimes."

"OK. Thanks," I said, getting up to go.

"You'll be coming back then?" she checked.

"Yes. I'll be back."

"Oh, that's good. I'm so pleased. He's a lovely old man. It's nice to think someone cares."

. . . . .

That night I sat on my bed and watched a moth flitting fretfully around the naked light bulb in my room.

I couldn't believe Dadda had been so close to me for all those years. It wasn't inconceivable that I might have seen him during that time; passed him on the street or stood next to him in a shop. I wouldn't have known.

I assumed he would have visited the Lauras' grave when he first got back from Australia and it pleased me to think he had found it in good order. I wondered if he ever asked himself who had looked after it while he was away; or if he ever stood in front of 163 and remembered his life there and thought about me.

To think we were so close... If only I had known six years earlier when he still had all his senses. I could have got to know him again and done something in return for all he did for me. But now it was too late. What could I do for him now?

I lay back on my bed and tried to imagine meeting him at a time before he had lost his faculties; tried to imagine our joy at finding each other again after all those years. What would we have said?

And then, out of nowhere, for one of the very few times in my life I thought about my natural father. I wondered if he had ever passed me on the street as I played outside Dadda's house on Manning Road; or if I might have had contact with him over the last ten years. I had never had any interest in knowing who he was, and had no way of finding out anyway, but it occurred to me that he might still be living in the area. Maybe I passed his house on the way to work every day. Or bought my cans of beer from him. Or maybe I had buried him. I would never know.

At which point the thought struck me that that was the one thing I could do for Dadda; when his time came I could bury him. But then I remembered he wanted to be cremated.

......

The next time I visited Dadda I found him in his room.

On the cupboard next to his bed was a plastic tumbler, a plastic water jug with a mustard yellow lid and, in a battered wooden frame, a grainy photograph of a young couple. At first I assumed it was Dadda and Laura but, on closer inspection, I couldn't see anything recognisable about the man in the picture. Maybe it was Dadda's father and Nanna.

I wandered around his room, picking up and examining the few personal belongings he had. Apart from the photograph there was nothing that gave any clues about his past.

While I was pottering a young nurse burst in with something in her hand.

"Mr. Stanmore's run off with your lizard again Mr. Preskett. Oh! God!" she yelped, startled by my presence. "Oh, I'm sorry, you gave me a fright. I didn't realise he had a visitor."

"That's OK. I'm sorry if I made you jump."

"It's my fault," she insisted. "Racing 'round like a lunatic!"

"What's that you've got there?" I asked, pointing to the object in her hand.

"This? Oh, it's just an old wooden carving of Mr. Preskett's. Mr. Stanmore's taken a shine to it. He thinks it's his 'pussycat'," she chuckled with a raise of her eyebrows.

"Can I see it?" I asked.

"Sure. It lives on the windowsill," she told me and handed it over.

In my adult work-hardened hands it felt smaller than I remembered it. A couple of spines on the back had been broken off and the forked tip of the tail was missing but it was undoubtedly my dragon. I knelt next to Dadda and held it up in front of him.

"Dadda? Do you remember this? You made it. Do you remember the story? The oak trees on the little hill? When their roots reached the dragon he would wake from his sleep. We sat under the oak trees, Dadda; you and me. Remember?"

Nothing. I sat back on my heels and searched his expressionless eyes.

"What happened, Dadda?" I asked hopelessly.

As I squatted there, scrutinising Dadda's face, another old man wandered in from the corridor.

"Where's my pussycat? Have you seen my pussycat?" he whined, before seeing the dragon in my hand and demanding: "That's my pussycat! Give it back!"

Watching him shifting from foot to foot, agitated, dishevelled and disoriented, I was reminded of the elderly lady shuffling down the ward when Dadda and I visited Nanna in hospital. I was reminded of Dadda's discomfort and the pained expression on his face as he sat next to Nanna's bed; and of how withdrawn he was in the pub afterwards. There, in the old people's home I looked into his face, both lined and blank at the same time, and I remembered his words.

"You were right Dadda; so cruel. So cruel."

He blinked at me, tugged his lapels and scratched his cheek weakly with his forefinger.

"Here's your pussycat," I said, giving the carving to Mr. Stanmore.

He took the dragon, cradled it in the crook of his arm and stroked it lovingly as he shambled back to his own room. At the end of my visit I told one of the nurses to let him keep it. It obviously meant more to him now than it did to Dadda.

.....

Over the next couple of months I took Dadda out whenever I could, trying to find something that might stir his memory and spark him back to life.

As we walked, painfully slowly, along Manning Road I hoped he might stop outside 163 or turn instinctively at the front gate or the entry, but we passed by as though it were just another house.

In the park we sat on a bench at the foot of the sledging slope.

"It's all changed since we used to come here, Dadda," I told him. "The bandstand used to be over there."

I pointed to a timber and hardboard half-tube that was being used by kids on skateboards and roller blades.

"The pond's been drained. And that stand of birch didn't used to be there."

He looked at some of the things I was pointing out to him but the only thing that seemed to catch his interest was the sound of children playing on the adventure playground; from time to time he'd turn on the bench and look over at them.

"Do you want to go over there?" I asked, but he became distracted, fiddling clumsily with the buttons on his overcoat.

"I don't suppose you remember Christmas morning, do you

185

Dadda? The snow? The sledge you made me?"

His hands fell into his lap and he watched a male pigeon chasing a female across the grass in front of us.

I took him to visit the Lauras' grave. I took him to the site where the building company he used to work for had its yard; it's a garden centre now but the buildings around it haven't changed. I took him into a couple of the local pubs. I took him out into the countryside and we had a picnic in a small wood, surrounded by wispy grass and pretty star-shaped flowers. I tried everything I could think of but nothing I did brought any kind of response from him. In the end I had to accept that Dadda had disappeared somewhere and it didn't look like he was ever coming back. All that was left to do was to help care for him in any way I could.

8

The last time I saw Tom in friendly circumstances was about six weeks ago.

We sat in our usual place in The Grouse, having a drink and a chat, but the atmosphere was a bit subdued. His favourite canary, Pippa, had been under the weather over the previous couple of days and he was worried about her.

"I'd hate to lose her just yet," he told me, sadly. "I've only had her six months. She's a lovely little thing; beautiful song and a lovely, friendly nature."

He always spoke of his birds like they were people which, I suppose, they were to him. He finished his pint and stared into his empty glass.

"I'll get them in, shall I?" I asked.

"Yeah," he replied, holding out his glass and adding philosophically: "Ah, well. Life goes on."

When I got back from the bar he asked how things were going with Dadda.

"Oh, I don't know... He doesn't really know who I am or what's going on," I told him. "He doesn't remember anything."

"It's sad, isn't it?" he sympathised. "I had it with my mum. She lost it completely towards the end."

He sipped his beer meditatively.

"Did I ever tell you about the time I hit a deer?" he asked.

I shook my head.

"I was driving through the New Forest, on my way back from a twitchers' convention. It was dusk and the roads were pretty empty. I wasn't going particularly fast; I never do. I suppose I might have been daydreaming a bit, but even if I hadn't been I doubt I could have done much about it… As I was driving along this deer suddenly shot out of the trees in front of me. I hit the brakes and swerved, trying to avoid it but, just when I thought I'd missed it, I clipped it and it rolled up onto the bonnet of the car. It came right up onto the windscreen; I thought it was going to shatter, but it didn't. Then it rolled back onto the road and carried on running. For a moment I thought it wasn't hurt but then, just before it disappeared into the trees, I noticed its hind leg was dangling as it ran. It was obviously broken, probably in several places. I got out to check the car but, apart from the tiniest dent on the front of the bonnet, there was no damage. I couldn't believe it. I got back in and pulled off the road. And I sat there. I didn't know what to do. The poor thing was lying out there somewhere, suffering. I felt terrible. It was getting darker by the minute but I couldn't leave. I stayed there for about an hour until a police car stopped to see if I was in trouble. I explained to the policemen what had happened and they said they'd tell a local gamekeeper. They said with any luck he'd be able to find it, probably in the morning, and put it out of its misery; assuming it was still alive by then. And I remember thinking if I'd had a gun I'd have gone into the forest and done it myself."

He took another drink.

"And there were times towards the end when I felt exactly the same about Mum."

"Did she suffer then?" I asked.

"No, I don't think so, not physically. But what kind of life did she have? None. I tell you what, Mason, we all have times when things go wrong and it seems like they'll never get better; but they do. And no matter how bad things get we still have the capacity to experience joy. It's been proven time and time again throughout history. And that's what we have to hang on to; while we have that capacity it's worth carrying on."

"So what about your mother?"

"Ah, well… Unfortunately, by the end, Mum wasn't capable of consciously experiencing anything, emotional or physical."

I thought about this for a moment.

"Joy?" I asked him.

"Yes. We all find joy in something don't we? For me it's my birds. For you it's… what? Free beer?"

I gave him a look and raised my glass but he stopped me before I had a chance to drink.

"And that's why I could never commit suicide. Before I got to the stage Mum was at I'd still have hope. Beyond that stage I wouldn't realise and it'd be too late. But if I ever ended up like her I'd be happy for someone to do it for me. I wouldn't want to live like that."

"I can't imagine anyone would," I agreed.

After that the atmosphere was even more sober, despite the rest of the drinks we put away. When we left the pub we said goodnight and I watched Tom walk away. Just as he was about to turn a corner I called out to him.

"Tom!"

"Yeah?" He turned back, an expectant look on his face.

"I hope Pippa's OK."

And he smiled for the first time that evening

"Thanks. See you Mason," he called back and waved as he turned away again.

And that was the last time I saw him as a friend.

.....

"You should cherish your friends, Mason. Especially your 'real' friends," Dadda told me.

We had just spent an afternoon in the company of Big Mick who had been in a particularly expansive mood, cracking jokes and horsing around. After he'd gone Dadda and I shared a warm glow that stayed with us into the evening.

"'Real' friends are worth hanging on to," Dadda continued.

"Because they're the friends who'll look after you, without question and without expecting anything in return. Don't ever forget that son."

.....

About a week after that sombre evening in The Grouse And Gun I was cleaning some headstones near the gates of St. Angela's when Tom turned up with a funeral party. As he supervised the removal of the coffin from the hearse I caught his eye and nodded a greeting, but he seemed to ignore me. I was a bit surprised because, while he obviously had to retain his professional decorum, he usually acknowledged me if he saw me around. However I didn't think too much of it; maybe he hadn't seen me. I went over to my shed to put on a brew as he often came and joined me for a quick cuppa while the service was being performed but, on this occasion, he didn't show. Again I wasn't unduly concerned, but when the same thing happened a couple of days later I wondered.

The next time he was at St. Angela's, about a week later, I went and found him standing with his colleagues by the cars of the funeral cortege.

"Tom!" I called but he blanked me, blatantly turning away and engaging in conversation.

This time I was surprised, shocked in fact, and I walked right up to him.

"Tom? Are you all right?" I asked.

"I'm fine thanks. I'm just a bit busy," he replied curtly.

"Oh! OK. Well, I'll get on then. See you down the Grouse on Saturday?"

"No. In fact you won't be seeing me down there again. Ever!" And he walked away, making a big thing of polishing the handles of one of the car doors.

I was astonished. I even considered going to his house that night, something I'd never done before, but I didn't because I know how much he likes his privacy.

A week and a half passed before I saw him again. He had been to the presbytery to see Father Courtenay and I intercepted him on his

189

way to the gates.

"Tom? What's wrong? Is something the matter?" I asked, deeply concerned.

"I don't want to talk to you," he replied and tried to push past.

"What is it? Is it something I've done? What's happened?"

He looked at me searchingly.

"You don't know?" he asked.

"No, I promise you. What is it?"

He took a deep breath and had a good look around to see no one else was within earshot. When he spoke it was very quietly and he was clearly finding it difficult to control himself.

"My house has been broken into..."

"Oh, Tom! I'm sorry. Was anything valuable...?"

He raised his hand sharply to silence me.

"My house has been broken into. Things have been taken, nothing really important, but all of my birds were... destroyed..."

"Oh, no..." I began but before I could express my sorrow he slapped me across the face.

"Will you shut up?!" he snapped. "My birds have all been killed and their blood was used to scrawl slogans on my walls."

His eyes were burning into me.

"Slogans? What slogans?" I asked hesitantly.

I could see he was hardly able to speak the words.

"'Gay fucker'. 'Queer bastard'. Things like that," he whispered.

He was still glaring at me as though he wanted to kill me.

"What? Hang on a minute, Tom... You don't think I had anything to do with it, do you?"

He continued staring, looking like he was about to explode.

"Tom? You're my friend..."

"Not any more I'm not!"

"You don't really think...?"

"No, I don't think you actually did this... thing. But you must have told someone about me."

"Tom I would never tell anyone anything..."

"So how did they find out? Huh? You're the only one who knows. I never told anyone else!"

I was speechless. Not only because of what had happened but

190

because Tom would think I would betray his confidence.

"Who would I tell?" I asked in my defence. "I don't talk to anyone except you."

"How do I know who you talk to when you've been drinking? And you're always drinking, aren't you Mason? We both know that!"

"But why would I tell anyone…?"

"How should I know? But more to the point; how could anyone else have found out? Answer me that!"

And I couldn't. If he asked me now I still couldn't. I might be able to come up with some ideas but at the time I was so shocked I stood before him, stunned into silence. Eventually I shrugged ineffectually and started murmuring something but, as far as Tom was concerned, my silence had spoken volumes.

"Exactly! You can't. So it must have been you," he spat the words at me.

"Tom, believe me, I would never…" I began but his mind was already made up.

"That's it! It's over. I never want to speak to you again. If you see me don't try talking to me because I'll ignore you. And I won't be going down the pub any more; I'll find somewhere else to drink. As it is I'm going to have to move away from here. I can't stay now… Not any more. Thanks to you!"

He brushed me aside and hurried out of St. Angela's without a backward glance.

…..

"Why is Mick your best friend?" I asked Dadda.

"That's a tough one," he replied. Then, after a few seconds' thought: "It's hard to put into words. We don't necessarily like all of the same things, Mick and me; and we certainly don't agree about everything but… We understand each other in a way no one else does. We're comfortable with each other. And we trust each other. Oh, there's more to it than that… You'll know what I mean when you find a 'real' friend."

And I thought I knew when I got to know Tom. Of the few friendships I have had in my life I particularly cherished my friendship with him. I would never have done anything to jeopardise it and I thought he would have realised that, but obviously not.

9

A few days after Tom ended our friendship so finally Father Courtenay dropped another bombshell.

It was a warm lazy day. I was spreading gravel, filling bare patches in the main drive, lost in the easy monotony of the work; shovelling the stones into the wheelbarrow, then from the barrow onto the drive. While I worked Father Courtenay came through the gates, nodding approval as he crunched his way towards the presbytery.

"Good morning, Mason," he called as he approached.

I raised a hand in greeting and wheeled the empty barrow over to the pile at the side of the church.

"Lovely day," he added, making a detour towards me.

He stopped behind me, watching for a minute as I filled up again.

"Mason, can I have a quick word?" he asked, a little uncomfortably.

I hefted a final load into the barrow and rested on the handle of my shovel.

"Yes Father?"

"I was having dinner with the Griffiths' last Sunday, Mason. Mrs. Griffiths mentioned that her son, Andrew, will be coming home from university in a couple of weeks. She was saying how hard it is for students to get holiday work these days and, errrm... Well, the Griffiths' do a lot of good work for the church, so I was thinking..."

He stopped for a moment and took a deep breath as though bracing himself.

"I happen to have a bit of spare money in the coffers," he continued, "and I had been thinking of looking into these government training schemes... But I thought, as a favour to the Griffiths', and to help you out, we could give young Andrew a job for the summer. See how things go. Maybe then you'd be able to take a proper holiday for once."

I was taken aback by this suggestion but I was even more shocked by his next statement.

"I've noticed things getting a little untidy here and there around the grounds. I realise you've been spending time with your stepfather; and that's perfectly understandable and acceptable. I have absolutely no problem with that. But maybe you could do with a bit of a hand…"

"I'm sorry Father, but which bits are untidy?" I interrupted him.

"Oh, I don't know, Mason. It's more of a general impression I got the other day, that's all; that things are getting just a touch ragged."

"I'm not sure I know what you mean Father but I promise you I can take care of things on my own."

"Well, Mason, that's as may be, but I've already told Mrs. Griffiths that Andrew can have a couple of weeks to see how he gets on. If it doesn't work out then, fine, no harm done. He'll start in three weeks. That should give you time to work out how best to employ him."

He nodded to indicate the conversation was over.

"Oh, by the way," he added as he turned to go, "the drive's looking much better."

When he'd gone into the presbytery I took a walk around the grounds and considered everything he'd said. For a start I had no idea he knew about Dadda. I thought I had managed to keep my private life totally separate from work. It just went to show how difficult it is to have secrets or privacy.

More alarming was the idea that I had been negligent in my work; but as I walked around I had to admit there were signs of neglect in one or two areas. Nothing substantial and nothing that I couldn't put right with a bit of attention, but it bothered me that I had let my standards slip. I took pride in my work and felt I had let myself down.

But even more disturbing was the prospect of having to work with someone; supervising him, explaining how to do things and spending breaks with him. I liked my job precisely because I didn't have to deal with people, apart from Father Courtenay, and I could go days without seeing him.

It was with a heavy heart that I returned to the task of patching up the drive.

.....

The following Sunday I took Dadda to visit the Lauras' grave. While I knelt down to do a bit of tidying he stood vacantly on the path, like a lost soul. I chatted to him idly as I pulled weeds and cleared away litter.

"You said you only liked to remember the good things about Laura, Dadda. Her laughter. Happy memories. And now you can't remember her at all."

I looked around to see if he was listening but he had wandered over to the standpipe at the end of the row. He was filling an old plastic bottle that was left lying next to the tap. I watched him carry it back along the row, thinking he'd got it for the Lauras' grave, but he shuffled to a grave further along and poured the water over a dead potted geranium standing at the foot of the tombstone.

"I think it's a bit late for that one Dadda," I said. "A bit too late."

I turned back to give the stone chippings a final rake, spreading them evenly with my hand. As I did the sun burst out from behind a cloud, shining brightly on the Laura's headstone, and I heard Dadda trip and fall on the path behind me. He didn't make a sound; he just lay there like a crumpled sack. I rushed over and helped him carefully back to his feet. A couple of small stones had imbedded themselves into the heel of his right hand but, other than that, he seemed unhurt. I took out my handkerchief, wiped a trickle of blood from his hand and held it in mine, staring down at it, feeling helpless and hopeless.

"I think it's time to say 'goodbye' Dadda," I whispered.

I looked into his eyes before taking him gently by the elbow and steered him away from the Lauras' grave for the last time.

On the bus back to Fairfields I wondered where someone's personality goes to when senility strikes. Does it just disappear? Or is it somehow locked away inside them? Whatever the case; the Dadda I knew seems to be lost forever; and with him has gone all dignity, feeling and understanding.

194

10

Since I started digging graves at St. Angela's I have led a simple existence.

My needs are basic and easily met.

My job is demanding and, until Father Courtenay made his recent observations, it has given me a certain amount of satisfaction. In some respects I suppose I could say that my job has become my life. I have never taken a proper holiday because I wouldn't know what to do with all that spare time these days.

'The man is a gravedigger and the gravedigger is the man.'

I still go swimming sometimes, early on Sunday mornings. Occasionally I'm the first one in and I'm able to enjoy having the pool to myself for a few minutes.

I like working in the rain; to feel it pouring over me, rivulets running from my hair across my face or trickling down my neck and the back of my shirt. It's a fresh clean feeling.

And I like the cold. I like to rest after a good hard stint of digging and feel the chill air creep through my clothes, wrapping itself around me, cooling the sweat on my skin.

I'm not so bothered about hot weather, it's too soporific; although I like the sun, especially watching the way its light plays on water or creates patterns as it streams through the leaves and branches of the trees.

I like the open air but I also like shutting myself away in my room, listening to a favourite piece of music while I read a good book.

I used to like to watching Tom telling stories; his soft, pink hands fluttering like the wings of the birds he loved so much as he gesticulated for emphasis and illustration.

I like to hold interesting objects in my hands; to feel their texture and shape and history.

And I have learned to like my own hands; calloused, hardened and swollen from years of honest graft.

"Do you actually bother with a shovel?" Tom asked once.

Sometimes I imagine the hand of a small boy slipping into mine, his small smooth fingers running over my fingers and palms, exploring the lines and creases, the two scars on my right hand, the hairs around the knuckles and the chipped, scratched nails.

And I like drinking beer and whisky.

But I can't honestly say there is anything about my life that fills me with joy. Maybe I've forgotten how to feel it.

11

If the real Dadda is locked away inside the little old man at Fairfields I haven't been able to find the key to release him, so I am going to set him free more finally; a decision I took after he fell at the Lauras' grave.

By taking his life I will be committing a crime, as far as 'society' is concerned, and I don't want to run away from that; I've had enough of running away. But, equally, I don't want to be put in prison, which is the obvious consequence of my actions. It's one thing to live in isolation but another thing entirely to live in confinement. I couldn't endure that, so I have decided to join Dadda. I'm going to return us both to nature.

This decision wasn't hard to make in the light of everything that's happened over the last four months. I have looked long and hard at my 'life' and realised it is no life at all. The things that were most important to me – Dadda, Tom, my job, my pride – have been taken away. I have no ties, no dreams and no goals. What kind of life is that?

And I have no one to mourn me so I won't be doing anyone any harm.

When I found Dadda I asked myself what I could do for him. I have an answer now: I can sacrifice myself to give him peace and, in so doing, find peace myself.

.....

In the two weeks since that last visit to the Lauras' grave I have made all the necessary preparations.

I have worked extra hours to get everything at St. Angela's back into peak condition. Mrs. Griffiths' son starts next week so, hopefully, he can keep things in good order until they appoint my successor.

I have written a letter to Father Courtenay, explaining everything and enclosing a cheque to pay for a new shed and any other inconvenience caused. I priced the shed at Bill Barlow's but knowing Father Courtenay he'll get it at a discount.

I have no intention of leaving any money to the church so I have written a cheque that will empty my savings account and I have sent it to Tom, asking him to dispose of it wisely if he won't keep it for himself. I have sworn my innocence in the matter of his secret and asked him to believe me; I hope he does.

…..

Today has been a strange day, starting when my shaving routine changed this morning. I have always followed the same pattern since I began shaving as a teenager – down the throat from left to right, up under the jowls, around the jaw-line and, finally, down the cheeks, upper lip and chin – but this morning, as I stared at my reflection in the mirror, I realised I had started on my cheek.

On my way home from work this afternoon I dropped in to Fairfields to let them know I'll be taking Dadda out tomorrow afternoon. I had with me the carving Dadda made of me as a young boy and, as we sat on a bench in the garden getting some fresh air, I took it from my bag, removed the cloth it was wrapped in and held it up in front of him.

"Do you remember this? It's me, Dadda; Mason. Do you remember?"

I put it in his lap and placed one of his hands on it. He stared at it for a few seconds, running his fingers over it, feeling its contours until a pair of blackbirds suddenly burst out of the bushes and chased each other, trilling and twittering across the lawn in front of us. He looked up to watch them but carried on absent-mindedly stroking the carving. And then he smiled. It was a fleeting moment, a flicker, nothing more, but I'm sure I saw his eyes light up for a second.

Was this because of the birds? Or was it some instinctive response to handling a well-crafted piece of wood? I don't know, maybe it was neither; but rather than finding hope in the moment it only served to harden my resolve, because a second later he was blank and unresponsive again.

.....

I went to the Grouse tonight in the vain hope that Tom might be there. I didn't have a book with me and after a couple of pints, when it seemed obvious he wouldn't turn up, I left. I walked home slowly, taking time to appreciate things I usually walked past without even noticing.

Back here in my room there is little left to do as I finish off the bottle of whisky I bought last night.

On the table in front of me are the things I will take with me, my most treasured possessions: Dadda's carvings; my photograph albums; my cameras; and my photography book. Looking at them now I'm amazed I still have them. I took them all around Europe with me and kept them in squats and rented rooms; they could so easily have been lost or stolen but, apart from the odd scratch or nick, they've all lived charmed lives.

.....

The forecast for tomorrow is sunny and dry.

When I get up I might bleach my hair, as I often do on a Sunday morning. Since I first started dying it ten years ago I have become almost obsessive about it. I suppose it's a form of vanity.

After that I need to go to St. Angela's to cut back a couple of low-hanging branches on the sycamore next to the shed; they're a bit too close for my liking and I'd hate to damage the tree.

Over the last fortnight I've been collecting scrap timber and deadwood which I've packed around a wooden platform I've built in the centre of the shed. I can add the sycamore branches to the pile.

At lunchtime I'll probably have a couple of pints somewhere before coming back to my room to collect my possessions.

About the time Father Courtenay is locking the cemetery gates I'll pick up Dadda from Fairfields and we'll take a taxi to St. Angela's, passing 163 on the way. As soon as we get to the shed I'll give him some sleeping tablets. Then we can sit outside, enjoying the birdsong and the evening sun, while we wait for the pills to take effect. When he starts to get drowsy I'll lay him on the platform and get him comfortable. Once I'm sure he's asleep I'll take a pillow and hold it over his face, pressing down firmly until I'm sure he is gone. Then I'll put the pillow under his head, fold his hands across his chest and place the carving of me beneath them.

Father Courtenay is always invited out to dinner on Sundays so I'll be safe posting the letter and my keys through the presbytery door. He won't be back until it's all over.

Back inside the shed I'll secure the door with a couple of sturdy padlocks I've fitted and I'll splash petrol over the piles of wood. I've packed in as much as I can to ensure an intense heat around the platform; Dadda always did like a good blaze. Then I'll sit on the platform and swallow the combination of drugs and alcohol I've prepared for myself. I've done some research into this and the mixture should be fast acting. Once it starts taking effect I'll throw a couple of lighted matches and lie down next to Dadda. There will be some physical trauma but it should be quite quick.

I hope I'll be gone before things get too hot – I have no desire to suffer any more than I need to – but if I do feel the flames licking around me before I lose consciousness, I'll be cooled by the image of a single precious moment: when a small boy and his Dadda stood hand-in-hand at the foot of a snow-covered hillside on a magical Christmas morning.

ALSO AVAILABLE ON I.M.P. FICTION

THE PEACOCK MANIFESTO
by Stuart David

Peacock Johnson's got an idea. A masterplan to help him escape his criminal past. But he needs someone who can turn ideas into something real, so he's taking his idea to America.

Join him on the craziest journey of your life, but a word of warning, don't fuck with Glasgow's own Rhinestone Cowboy, because nothing is going to stand in his way. Not the nagging of his mad missus, Bev, nor the weird antics of his Yankee sidekick, Evil Bob.

As Peacock careers from one crisis to another, his aspirations and plans spiral out of control in a frenzy of hilarity, disaster, sadness and insanity. But this is America, the land of dreams, where anything is possible, even The Peacock Manifesto...or is it?

The Peacock Manifesto weaves farce with danger, splicing sensitive undercurrents with brutal reality, sucking the reader into Peacock's well-dressed, badly advised and always utterly compulsive world.

"Run out at once and buy David's darkly hilarious second novel."
Dazed & Confused

"Fast and funny." *The Guardian*

"A riotous second novel. Pure fucking genius." *Uncut* - 5★

"A fantastic second outing for David, proving the author's continuing skills, as a fine comic writer." *ID* Magazine

ISBN: 0-9533275-5-8   Paperback, 160 pages Price: £7.99
Web. www.peacock-johnson.com

HARRY & IDA SWOP TEETH

By Stephen Jones

The darkly humourous second novel from maverick musician Stephen 'Babybird' Jones, author of the critically acclaimed debut, *The Bad Book*. Sixteen years ago from the day you are reading this, two babies were born Siamese. Joined at the head but then successfully separated, they like to think they have retained a little piece of each other's brain. A bit of Ida in Harry and a bit of Harry in Ida

Short of money, Harry and Ida Brick give themselves up for drive-in-drive-out laboratory rats, paid for injections of new 'Society Drugs' - cocktails of genes and DNA taken from the saliva of schizophrenics, offenders, vandals, and pregnant teenagers. Feeling like a couple of young gods, they go missing and with all the bad blood swirling round inside this duo of delinquent tornados, a strange and incredible journey begins to unfold. A dark and devious plot intertwined with chilling comic genius and freakishly potent imagery guarantees a unique and compelling read from this highly respected lyricist and wordsmith.

"Jones has decided to turn his distinctive hand to writing novels. The results are astonishing." *The Times*

ISBN 0-9533275-7-4 Paperback 176 Pgs £7.99

YOURS TRULY, PIERRE STONE

By Sam Bain

Written in letters from an obsessed fan to the TV game-show hostess he idolises, *Pierre Stone* is a black comedy about a man trapped in a state of arrested childhood, fed by the cathode ray nipple of his television set. His world is a comforting solar system where breakfast cereals, chocolate bars, video games and daytime TV shows orbit the life-giving sun of his game-show love. The fact that they've never met doesn't change a thing. She loves him, she understands him, and she'll always be there for him. When Pierre's mother dies, the girl inside the TV set becomes his world. Gradually it dawns on him that all this time, she hasn't been writing back. And he's not happy about it... *Pierre Stone* is a funny and disturbing look at a culture where minor celebrities are gods and *HELLO!* is the Bible. Web: www.pierrestone.com

"Somewhere between Adrian Mole and Travis Bickle."

Independent On Sunday

Sam Bain has written for many TV shows including *2DTV*, *Smack The Pony* and *TV To Go*.

ISBN 0 9533275 6 6 Paperback 176 pages £7.99

THE BAD BOOK
by Stephen Jones

Hit had been happy as an eight year old. He didn't want to grow up. He was a sweet kid, but one that wasn't quite right. He had juvenile insomnia. He was somewhere floating between ME and E–Number hyperactivity. Even the weird bulge under his eye didn't seem to worry him. He was just happy to fall off the edge of the world and get up again. But then his mother goes missing, and all of a sudden he has to be an adult.

This striking debut novel documents a pivotal two days in Hit's bizarre life. It is a desperate, and disturbing tale of one boy's fight to win back a normal life. To find his lost mother and keep tabs on his father, the man he suddenly realises he knows nothing about.

Stephen Jones is the musical blacksheep Babybird. *The Bad Book* is Stephen's first novel, and has nothing to do with music whatsoever.

"Astonishing. *The Bad Book* shares its grotesque childlike detail with Ian Banks' *The Wasp Factory*, but the bleak surreality and contorted memory sequences belong to Jones." *The Times*

"It is breathtaking in its simplicity and its originality. Jones simply has a gift for the sort of words you relish wrapping your tongue around." *The Scotsman*

"Cryptic, yet this cossetted, wounded loner in dystopia will come back to haunt you... 'til infinity." *ID* Magazine

ISBN: 0-9533275-3-1   Paperback, 124 pages   Price: £6.99
Web: www.babybird.co.uk

NALDA SAID
by Stuart David

Riddled by an intense fear of his bizarre secret being discovered, the narrator of *Nalda Said* grows up in the strange seclusion of a shoddy caravan with his Aunt Nalda, whose own colourful storytelling leaves him perpetually trapped between fantasy and reality.

Nalda's nephew eventually finds work as a hospital gardener where, perhaps for the first time, he finds true friendship and begins to realise that his dark secret has been suffocating what hope he had of ever leading a normal life.

Finding himself in love, this socially disjointed figure struggles to reconcile his own curious view of the world with the stark daily reality that most people are forced to live with. *Nalda Said* is a compelling and brilliantly crafted tale of one man's pained anxiety and desperate search for his dream - to live a normal life.

"Delicately written and achingly sad, with just a hint of a moral in the poignant denouement, if David ever gives up the day job, pop music's loss could well be literature's gain." *The Times*

"Dark undercurrents of dread and skillful thriller rush... There's an echo of Salinger in *Nalda Said*'s dissection of alienation." *NME*

"Beguiling and ever so slightly unsettling, this is the insular terrain of *The Wasp Factory* and *The Butcher Boy* compassionately revisited."

The Face

ISBN: 0-9533275-2-3 Paperback, 160 pages   Price: £7.99
Web: www.geometrid.co.uk

MILK, SULPHATE AND ALBY STARVATION
by Martin Millar

"What's allergic to milk, collects comics, sells speed, likes The Fall and lives in Brixton? Alby Starvation, the first true British anti-hero of the giro generation. Milk, Sulphate and Alby Starvation *is a strange and wonderful story of unbelievable allergies, seedy gutter violence and manic paranoia. I've yet to meet someone who has not enjoyed it."* NME

Your doctor refuses to believe you're allergic to just about everything, especially milk, there's a megalomaniac professor digging a hole outside your flat, your small stake in the amphetamine market in Brixton is being threatened by a mysterious Chinese man and the Milk Marketing Board have taken out a contract on your life. Welcome to the bizarre, obsessive world of Alby Starvation.

A world full of shop-lifting, death-threats, paranoia and video game arcades. Alby's frantic struggle to avoid being shot provides the hilarious and engaging back-drop for this, Martin Millar's debut novel.

"A welcome re-issue. This entertaining fable, which is alternately surreal and grubbily realistic, still delights." *The Times*

"Pop cultural references are everywhere in this frantic cultish debut which takes an Irvine Welsh-esque turn." *The Guardian*

"A masterful work that goes straight to the heart of a spurned generation. A work of rare genius and truly cult, it deserves a place on your book shelf next to Hubert Selby Jr's *Last Exit To Brooklyn*."

The List

"A minor classic... strange, quirky and entertaining to the end."

What's On London

ISBN: 0-9533275-4-X Paperback, 160 pages   Price £6.99
Web: www.martinmillar.com

THE TECHNO-PAGAN OCTOPUS MESSIAH
by Ian Winn

Part bizarre quest, part unique travelogue, part insane fiction, *The Techno-Pagan Octopus Messiah* is an extraordinary tale of prophetic dreams and adventurous treks through Egypt, Rajastan and northern India.

Winn disguises himself as a tourist and, catalysed by drugs from the Amazonian rain forest, takes the reader on a kaleidoscopic trip to places where crystals are dragon eggs, free love is expensive and tourist massacres mean discount hotels. Along the way lies among other things, a tantric commune, an illegal hike up the Pyramid of Chepren, and cryptic encounters with Indian snake saddhus.

Ian Winn is a leading star of the spoken-word circuit. His volatile performances have won high acclaim across both Britain and the USA.

"If you are looking for something a bit different this year, try Ian Winn's debut novel. It has all the travel fiction requisites in spades. Delivered with crazed enthusiasm and humour, it makes a refreshing change from the usual backpackers novels." *The Times*

"Inventive, brilliantly realised characters... displays a rampant thirst for mysticism and self-discovery. One can not help being won over by Winn's enthusiasm and intellectual energy." *The Sunday Times*

"The most progressive, alternative life-style novel of the decade."
Dream Creation

"One astonishing book!" *Select*

ISBN: 0 9533275 1 5   Paperback, 288 pages   Price: £7.99
Web: www.octopusmessiah.com

LOVE AND PEACE WITH MELODY PARADISE
by Martin Millar

This is the story of Melody Paradise. You'll like her – everybody does. Women aspire to be like her and men fall in love with her. Melody is kind, spiritual and very beautiful. She's also on a mission... and nothing is going to stand in her way.

The travelling community to which she belongs has become horribly fragmented by a series of mysterious and chaotic happenings. Her mission is to reunite them. She organises a festival as the perfect vehicle to bring them together, during which an amazing story unfolds, often funny, sometimes sad, always compelling... and with a twist in the tail.

Through the words and eyes of Martin Millar, the reluctant guest novelist at Melody's festival, we become privileged observers of a world most of us would struggle to even imagine.

"Brixton's answer to Kurt Vonnegut." *The Guardian*

"A charming tale... very funny." *Melody Maker*

ISBN: 0-9533275-0-7 Paperback, 288 pages   Price £6.99
Web: www.martinmillar.com

HOW TO ORDER:

Visit us at:

www.impbooks.com

for more information on titles, reviews, author biographies and our music book label, *Independent Music Press,* home to titles onDave Grohl, Stereophonics, Prodigy, David Bowie, Beastie Boys, Shaun Ryder and more.

For any queries or for a free catalogue,
e-mail us at: info@impbooks.com

TO PURCHASE BY POST

Please make cheques/postal orders or
international money orders payable in £Sterling to:
I.M.P. FICTION LTD
and send your payment to:

I. M. P. FICTION (PS)
P.O. BOX 14691,

LONDON SE1 2ZA

Please allow 21 days for delivery.
Postage and packing is FREE in the UK,
£1.50 for Europe and £3.00 for the Rest of the World.